PIGS IN THE PLAYGROUND

By the same author:

Calves in the Classroom

Pigs in the Playground

by
JOHN TERRY

illustrated by
HENRY BREWIS

Farming Press Ltd
Wharfedale Road
Ipswich

First published 1986
Reprinted 1988

ISBN 0 85236 158 0

British Library Cataloguing in Publication Data

Terry, John, *1952*–
   Pigs in the playground.
   1. Rural conditions——Study and teaching
   (Secondary)——England
   I. Title
   630'.7'1242   S535.G7

   ISBN 0-85236-158-0

Typeset by Galleon Photosetting, Ipswich
Reproduced, printed and bound in Great Britain by
Hazell Watson & Viney Limited,
Member of the BPCC Group,
Aylesbury, Bucks

This Is My Life . . .

I HAVE always been interested in animals – for as long as I can remember, in fact. From when I started to talk I was animal mad. I persuaded my parents to let me have pets just as soon as I was able to take care of them. I started with the inevitable goldfish, and graduated to puppies, some tropical fish and a budgerigar.

My aunt and uncle managed an eighty-acre farm about ten miles away. The lady who owned it lived in a large mansion house, and my uncle not only looked after the farm but also grew orchids for her and chauffeured her Rolls Royce and Lanchester. I spent many happy weekends helping them on the farm which they ran for the best part of thirty years. I can remember feeding the hens when I was only four years old. We start young, we farmers! I also fed the calves and even carried some hay around under my arm, like uncle used to do.

Farming was in my blood, and by the time I was fifteen I had kept rabbits, bantams, guinea pigs, tortoises, mice, hamsters, newts, lizards and frogs. Quite a little menagerie. Rabbits and guinea pigs were my particular speciality, and I used to exhibit these at local 'fur and feather' shows.

Next came birds. At one time I had as many as a hundred birds in aviaries in the back garden. I took especially to aviary-bred British birds, and exhibited firstly as a junior, then a novice, and finally rose to champion status. I won hundreds of prizes with them, including two 'firsts' at the National Exhibition of Cage Birds, held at Alexandra Palace, in London.

Whereas other teenagers tended to be interested in pop stars and football, I was interested in animals, birds and plants. I became a very active member of the local ornithologists' club, and would spend much of my free time out bird-watching.

As I grew older and stronger I was able to help uncle more and more on the farm. I would stay in their home over the weekends, and spent many holiday times working alongside them.

Eventually the old lady died and the estate passed into the hands of Lord Clifton, her nephew. He moved into the large mansion house, and in next to no time was expanding the enterprise through the purchase of three neighbouring farms, making a total of four farms and some five hundred acres. The establishment included a large dairy herd with one hundred and eighty cows, a beef unit, sheep, and a large acreage of wheat and barley. New tractors and a new combine harvester were acquired, and the whole enterprise took on a modern and progressive look. I was fascinated, and much of what I have learned about farming came from those early years.

When I left school at eighteen I hoped that Lord Clifton

2

might be able to offer me work. There were no full-time vacancies, however, so I went to work on a mixed farm of some 120 acres, two miles away from my home. The farmer was a real rough-and-ready type, a character named Mick Hardy. It was a contrast from what I had come to expect on Lord Clifton's progressive estate, and it took me a little while to adjust.

Mick was definitely one of the older generation of farmers, using worn-out equipment and taking a very primitive approach to stockmanship. He certainly did not farm intensively – apart from the thistles, that is. He raised a bumper crop of these, year in and year out.

This old-fashioned farm had twenty dairy cows, twenty heifers, fifteen beef cattle, twenty sheep, thirty pigs, fifty hens, a few potatoes and some wheat and barley. Although it was only a small operation he did a little bit of everything, so my education was right across the board – much better, in fact, than if I had been working on a more modern, specialised operation. As it happened, shortly after I arrived he suffered a heart complaint, so much of the day-to-day

work was left to me. Necessity is the best tutor – and I learned fast.

After my twelve months' practical work experience, I was accepted at Brooksby Agricultural College, Leicestershire, on a three-year OND course. At the same time, news came that I had been accepted at Worcester College of Higher Education on a three-year specialist Rural Studies Teacher's course. I thought long and hard about which to accept, and went finally for the Worcester course.

I never regretted my decision, and spent three very happy years at the college which had its own extensive flower, fruit and vegetable gardens, as well as an orchard and a small farm. In addition to rural studies, my course comprised of education, sociology, psychology, philosophy and the history of education. The rural studies course itself was split into ecology or environmental studies, agriculture and horticulture. I had to complete three blocks of teaching practice and produce numerous projects.

In 1974 I completed my studies, became qualified, and almost immediately a vacant post advertised in the *Times Educational Supplement* took my eye. It was for the Head of the Rural Studies Department at my old school in north Warwickshire. At first, I could not decide whether it would be wise to return where many of the staff, from the headmaster down, had known me as a pupil, and I was not sure how I would be received.

I went ahead though, was interviewed ... and was offered the job. The school was a comprehensive with about 950 pupils aged from twelve to sixteen. It had a teaching staff of fifty and an exceptionally fine academic record, with excellent examination results.

So there I was, back at the same old school but now one of the teachers. A teacher with a difference, though, for as well as my academic responsibilities I had set my heart on building a registered smallholding at the school. Something to be proud of one day.

Let me tell you how I fared; of the heartaches and headaches I faced in the early years, but also of the

4

exhilaration and enjoyment I – and many pupils – have had in making our dream a reality. We have had our fair share of thrills and spills, but some really profound successes too.

One thing I can say for certain: It has never been dull!

In the Beginning . . .

THE SCHOOL itself was not strange to me, of course. I still knew the layout of the classrooms and assembly halls, and so on. What was strange, though, was my situation.

Four years ago I had been a pupil, and the teachers had called me by my surname. Now I was a member of that staff, I sat on the other side of the desk, and pupils called me 'Sir'. I could not help feeling a little like the outlaw who had joined the posse!

There I was, teaching rural studies and science. Too much science, for my liking, and not enough rural studies – but there was not much I could do about that. Not just yet, anyway.

My rural studies department – grand though it sounded – consisted of one mobile classroom which badly needed painting inside and out. The classroom was tucked away on the far side of the playground, in splendid isolation. 'Townies' and the 'farming fraternity', that is what it was; us and them. I had inherited an old potting shed, too. It was situated over behind the gymnasium, two hundred yards away, across the 'no man's land' of the playground. It contained a motley assortment of garden tools which had seen better days. My text books had not only seen better days, they had actually lived through them! Many of them dated back to 1939. I say 'many of them' – but actually there were not many at all, old or otherwise.

I had an acre of land, a positive wilderness when I inherited it. There were, so I was told, a few vegetables growing in there – but you would have needed an intrepid native guide to hack your way through the weeds and find them. I did not fancy it. The soil, too, was heavy clay. It badly needed lime, fertilisers and manure. I was told that I had only fifteen students, all fifth-year. The previous year, as fourth-years, they had been given a small vegetable plot each, and told to look after it. One or two had obviously worked hard, and had managed a few vegetables to show for their labour.

They had had their problems during the year. There had been a bit of feuding going on – a bit like the middle ages. The wronged party had secretly vandalised the other fellow's plot. Then during the six-week break of the summer holidays Mother Nature had got the better of the lot of them, since no one had bothered to come along and tend their crops. They returned to find everything covered in weeds.

I needed a new start. I needed to get the pupils pulling together as a team without the feudal approach – the 'three acres and a cow' attitude – and introduce some new topics, interesting them not just in vegetable growing, but in ecology or environmental studies, agriculture and horti-culture. I planned to dig out a pond, and keep fish in it

and also use it to teach ecology or environmental studies. I would plant some British species of trees, and put up nesting boxes for birds. On the horticultural side, we would create lawns, lay out flower gardens, plant fruit trees and build a greenhouse.

The agricultural section would, I hoped, be the most exciting of all. It would mean not only growing a few rows of crops, for demonstration purposes, but actually building up a small farm, with livestock. I would not settle for a glorified allotment. I wanted a registered smallholding . . . and I was going to get it, or bust.

I wanted pedigree stock, something we could all be proud of, and I wanted to exhibit these at shows. Back in 1974 the subject of rural studies was for the less able pupils. They had had it drummed into them that since they were not clever enough for physics or chemistry, it was down to the 'digging department' for them. I had heard Mr Petty, the woodwork teacher, use this term in the staffroom – and on my very first day, too: 'I see we have a new "digging teacher". He has started work today. Well, he must be desperate for a job!' Two or three other members of staff had nodded agreement.

I could see that I was going to have my work cut out, but I was determined to put the department and the subject on the map; to involve all age groups and all ability levels in rural studies. I wanted pupils to take one lesson of rural studies in the second and third year (we have no first year at the school). Then I wanted to see it as an option in the fourth and fifth years, so that all interested pupils could pursue the subject. I intended to see it as an actual 'O' level examination subject – not just the existing CSE. I was also interested in writing my own CSE syllabus.

I was dreaming big, but I knew it could be done. All it needed was someone with the vision – and a lot of hard work.

The 'hard work' part of things started with those overgrown vegetable plots. The pupils and I got to work to clear the weeds. My frustration was that most of my

8

timetable was allocated to teaching science, so I had to fit in much of my other work either before school, at break times, or after school was over. Those weeds haunted me; I could not sleep for weeks because of them. I would wake up in the middle of the night dreaming of the things. I desperately needed to get it sorted out. I thought the local residents whose gardens backed onto our vegetable plot would appreciate that, too. Weed seeds had been blowing into their gardens, and twitch was creeping under the fence and attacking their meticulously kept lawns and borders. We were not their favourite people.

We were not the favourite people of the county council, either. They had given me one hundred pounds to spend on the department. I suppose they thought they had been generous, in their own way, but that amount of money was not going to go anywhere – not considering what I had planned. I had made a list of the essentials: spades, forks, rakes, hand forks, wheelbarrows, a greenhouse, garden cold frame, paving slabs, buckets, fencing, gates and so on and so on. Oh, and that did not include the livestock buildings I needed – and the livestock too! The list was growing longer and longer, the more I thought about it. I had forgotten the woodworking tools, feed troughs, vegetable seeds – not to mention the calves, sheep, pigs, goats, rabbits and hens. There was nothing else for it, I would have to telephone the county council.

I plucked up the courage, and gave them a ring. I explained the financial problem I faced. The 'pen pusher' in charge said 'sorry' but I could not possibly have any more money. I got out pen and paper and wrote a 'crawling' letter; the answer was the same. No chance.

Mind you, my calculations as to what I would need to spend to realise my dream had terrified me. Things were just so expensive. Even a simple item like a 3 ft by 2 ft paving slab would set me back a pound – and I needed five hundred of those. I worked it out. I was not going to get much change out of ten thousand pounds, and I was stuck with a measly one hundred.

So that was it. There was only one solution: I needed to become an expert scrounger. What I could not buy, I would have to beg, borrow or . . . No, as a teacher of young people, an exemplar for youth, I would have to stay on the right side of that particular line. But I was prepared to work – and work hard; prepared to make do and mend, and prepared to take other people's cast-offs and do them up. One day I would replace my ramshackle equipment with brand-new items, but not just now. That would have to wait.

I was a 'native' of the area, and had many friends connected with agriculture. That was an asset. I was a teacher, trying to set up a smallholding for educational purposes, not for commercial gain – and I reckoned that was an 'ace' card in my hand. I had been connected with the Young Farmers' Club since I was a teenager, and this year on my return from college I had been elected Chairman. That would open doors for me, too. I would get to meet many people that way. I began to feel a little more confident.

On my first day at school, the deputy headmaster, Mr Bell, warned me about a large man-trap which was situated in the middle of our vegetable garden. With a smirk he told me that the previous 'digging' teacher had almost come to grief in it. The way he looked me up and down worried me, just a little.

At lunchtime I searched the garden for it. The trap had been dug by the fifth-year pupils. It was quite a hole, some five feet square and four feet deep with steep sides, and the whole thing was covered with branches, with turf laid on the top. Because of the long hot summer, the turf had yellowed, but at the end of the previous term it must have been well camouflaged. Two of the ring-leaders of the plot, Steven Wood and Martin Towers, had positioned themselves behind the hole, then called over their teacher. Not suspecting a thing, he had walked towards them, then vanished down the hole. The whole class had been watching, and the poor teacher never lived it down. I was

grateful for the tip-off. I did not need that sort of start to my teaching career!

As it happened, the man-trap turned out to be quite useful. It became the last resting place of all my rubbish. Rocks, weeds, rotten vegetables, even an old bike frame went down into the depths, never to return. Every spare moment I had was spent on that piece of land. I got backache, pulling and forking weeds. If it had not been for a group of pupils who pitched in to help, it would have taken forever. As soon as we had finished weeding, we dug the whole plot over.

For homework I gave my pupils the assignment of designing and laying out their ideal rural studies department. It had to include facilities for ecology or environmental studies, a horticultural section – with lawns, flower beds, vegetables and fruit – and an agricultural section, with farm livestock. I got some excellent pointers from this, and we selected the best ideas for our final plan.

I wanted a nice view of lawns and gardens from the

classroom, with the livestock buildings within easy access for rainy days. We got quite involved in the planning, and I could sense that they had caught my enthusiasm too. I spent the whole of one evening outside with a tape measure getting all the relevant dimensions. Then I transferred these to a huge piece of graph paper, drawing it all to scale. On it we marked the site of the flower garden, the vegetable plot, the paddocks, the fruit garden and the location for our livestock buildings.

It was all taking shape nicely. We had a long way to go, but we had made a start.

Cleaning Out the Cowshed

MY FIRST few days at the school were busy learning the 'educational ropes'. I had to memorise the pupils' names, their forms, my class groups, the assembly pattern, house system, syllabus ... the list seemed never-ending. At the same time I was trying to spend every available moment pulling and forking out weeds from the 'wasteland'.

After a few days of being treated as something of an oddity – a spare part in the educational framework – I realised that I had to do something dramatic. If I was going to develop my rural studies department and have people take me seriously, I needed something to attract attention, something that would put me on the map. I decided that livestock was the answer.

I needed something large; something no other school in the area had. A pony would be a good choice to encourage the pupils and win them over with free rides. I toyed with the idea, but dismissed it. A pony is not a real 'agricultural' animal – and I needed credibility as well as popularity. No, it would have to be something strictly agricultural; no pets or zoo animals, but a true farm animal.

I wondered about an orphaned lamb – a cade lamb, as they are called. That would have been ideal, but it was September and there are not many lambs around at that time of year. I have always liked pigs, but they are hardly the best animal to start with – too much 'mucking out' and downright hard work. I could not see myself getting many volunteers for that. Poultry was next on my list. No, the pupils would feel they were boring.

A calf. It had to be a calf, I just knew it; or two calves, if I could afford it. I was not keen on the idea of bidding for two calves at our local market where dealers tend to dominate the bidding. They would probably 'run me up', which would mean that I would end up paying over the odds. I needed a couple of strong, healthy animals. I just could not risk one of them not thriving, which definitely would not have been good for the image. I only had the council's hundred pounds to spend. Buying privately, from a trustworthy local farmer, seemed to be the only answer.

I telephoned Lord Clifton. He was very helpful, and agreed to sell me two strong Friesian bull calves, ten days old, for just ten pounds each. Calves were cheap to buy in 1974 – but even allowing for that, he was certainly doing us a favour.

I agreed to go and have a look at them that evening. The way Lord Clifton had described the calves, it sounded as though the inspection would only be a formality, but this would be my very first expenditure on the farm and – like most farmers – I had to be careful.

I had not yet officially met my rural studies group – fifteen lads – all 'less able' pupils, as they are euphemistically called. One or two of them had introduced themselves to me, however – and I had found many volunteers to help me fork out the weeds outside class hours. One lad I had met was a 'hard case' named Clive Gibson, who I was told, had been 'done' for 'grievous bodily harm'. Fine.

A wizened old veteran of the teaching profession had once told me that the way to get the respect of a class was to pick out the biggest, toughest lad – then really make him look silly in front of his classmates. There may be some merit in such an approach, but when you are five-foot-nothing you have to be very careful whom you pick on! Even some of our girl pupils are built like Russian shot-putters.

It was obvious from the outset that Clive was a dishonest rogue. He even bragged about it. 'Clive, why have you turned out so bad?' I asked him one day.

'It's not my fault. I fell in with bad company, at an early age.'

'But you're only fifteen, now. Who was this bad company?'

'My Mum and Dad, Sir,' he replied, with a big grin. I believed him.

I reckoned my best tactic was to try to get Clive on my side. If I could get him interested in the farm it might help keep him out of mischief. I asked him if he would like to come over to Lord Clifton's farm with me, and look over the calves. He seemed surprised – but pleased – and quickly accepted. I hinted that if he took to the calves he could become one of the pupils looking after them. He smiled. First round to me.

We went over to the farm that evening. We watched the calves being fed, and they drank the milk easily without any help from the stockman. To get baby calves to drink from a bucket, the stockman will first let the calves suck his fingers in the milk. Clive had never set foot on a farm before, and had certainly not touched farm livestock. He was spellbound. The calves were all that Lord Clifton had said – enormous for their age, and very strong. I thanked him, and he agreed to deliver them later that evening. Things were going well.

We had no agricultural buildings at the school, only the old potting shed, measuring twelve feet by eight feet, out of the department's area behind the gym. On my second day I had found some willing volunteers (as opposed to unwilling volunteers!) and we had cleaned out the shed. Not that there was much in there – two dustbins, one empty and one half-full of potting soil, a couple of rakes, a few spades – mostly with broken handles – and a couple of forks with prongs missing. We moved the dustbins outside, shifted the garden tools, and swept the floor. Then we scrubbed it clean with Jeyes Fluid, leaving the door and windows open so that it would soon dry.

Clive and I got back to school and waited for the calves. After about an hour the Land Rover arrived, loaded right up. In the back were two calves, two bags of substitute calf milk, two bags of calf weaner pellets and three bales of straw – everything I needed, in fact, except hay. We unloaded the calves, then I stored the feed in my classroom. I used two bales of straw for bedding, and left the third bale in the corner of the pen, ready for when the bedding needed replacing. Lord Clifton let me have the feed and straw at cost price, and charged me nothing for delivery. I thanked him very much; he left . . . and the calves were ours. We had started farming!

The next morning I could not see the calf-shed for pupils. They were pushing and shoving to have a look through the windows and get a glimpse of our new arrivals. The shed made an excellent calf building. It was big enough, draught-proof and well ventilated. I scrounged a couple of buckets and started to mix up the calf milk. I had about fifty volunteers to do the feeding – everyone wanted to try his or her hand. Clive fed one – revelling in his new-found station – and I fed the other.

I had to explain to the pupils that the animals were not pets, and that we would have to sell them when they reached about five or six months old. At that stage they would simply have outgrown the accommodation we had available. I told them that we would study the calves, measuring them each week, and hoped to learn all we could from them. Once they were sold, we would look to buy more baby calves.

The calves really took to the milk – with an audience witnessing every gulp. I smiled to hear comments like: 'I wish I was taking rural studies', and 'how can you change from biology to rural studies?' My cunning plan seemed to be working.

The next task was to pick names for our new acquisitions. I was showered with possibilities – Bonnie and Clyde, Bill and Ben, and so on. We picked the names the next day, choosing something simple and descriptive. One of the calves had a pink nose, and the other a black one. We called them Pinkie and Blackie – confident that we would always get the names right.

People were now beating a trail to my door. The deputy head and . . . yes . . . the headmaster, Mr Beech, put in an appearance. I even caught Mr Petty, the woodwork teacher responsible for the 'digging department' tag, taking a sly peek.

My next job was to contact the press. I called five of the local papers and every one sent a reporter and, in most cases a photographer, to cover the story. They took pictures of the calves and the pupils and did a whole series of interviews. The pupils became 'famous' overnight; they loved it! We made front page news in the area, with headlines like 'School Starts Farming'. Word was relayed from 'on high' that the headmaster was 'pleased'. That was worth a couple of house points, I can tell you.

I now needed to turn my attention to the provision of more foodstuff for the animals. I needed some hay, and did not want to spend any more of my precious county council money than I absolutely had to. I went to see Mick, my old farm boss – a real rough diamond. He always made plenty of hay, and I thought I might just be able to put the 'screws' on him. I knew it would not be easy, though. Mick was, shall we say . . . careful with his money.

I arrived at his farm at around lunch-time – the only time I could get off from school. I noticed a strange car in the farmyard, and thought it must be a sales rep. He used to delight in reducing them to pulp and it was rare for any rep to make a sale on that farm.

I could hear raised voices from the direction of the

cowshed. No modern milking parlour for Mick, this was your actual old-fashioned cowshed, a brick-built long, low building where twenty cows were tied up in standings, with a manger in front. They all stood facing the wall, so that their backsides dropped dung into a channel behind them. Behind them, too, was a passageway along which the cows moved in and out of the shed. Each cow had its place, and moved there, unerringly, after returning from the pasture.

The cows were milked twice a day, with the original milking machines – the covered bucket sort, with teat cups connected on top. Mick was not really into modern technology. When the cows had been milked, the milk would be tipped out of the bucket, into a churn. A milk cooler was then placed in the churn, the cooler connected to a tap, and water passed through metal pipes, cooling the milk.

I had worked on the farm for a year, and used to clean this cowshed out twice a day. I took pride in my work and in the nice clean shed. It was three years since I had been back there – and I was not prepared for the sight that met me. It was terrible! The top part of the walls were black with dirt and cobwebs – but the farther down you looked, the worse it got. At the foot of the wall it was a good inch and a half thick in cow muck. I stood there, aghast. After all the work I had done!

The voices were louder now. A lady in a woollen jumper, a tweed skirt and wellington boots was haranguing Mick. She had a clipboard in her hand, and the expression on her face was dynamite.

'Now Mr Hardy, this cowshed is really disgusting! The walls have not been cleaned since my last visit; the place is filthy. You are a registered, licensed milk producer, and yet you are producing milk in these sort of conditions. It really isn't good enough . . . and I can't let it go on!' The menace in her voice was all too real. 'The floor hasn't been swilled down for ages . . . I'm totally disgusted!' I was nodding away to myself, agreeing with her every word. The woman was obviously an inspector. I later found out she was a Miss Smart, from the Ministry of Agriculture.

Cleaning Out the Cowshed

It is usual practice to milk the cows in the morning, turn them out, shovel out the muck, then swill down with a hose pipe and yard brush. After the afternoon milking the whole process would be repeated. Mick had been taking a few 'short cuts'.

By this time, the inspector was checking the milking machines. I looked over her shoulder and could see that they were a strange yellowish colour inside. They badly needed a good sterilising. Likewise, the milk cooler needed a bit of attention.

'Really! This just won't do, Mr Hardy,' she reproached, scribbling away furiously on her clipboard.

19

'Well . . . er . . . I've sacked three men since John left . . .' he blustered. 'They were all bone-idle, and just didn't get on with me . . . not like John. He was a good lad.' I was still nodding.

This was the first time, to my knowledge, that Mick had ever praised me. He never gave praise . . . he never gave anything, for that matter; against his principles. Or is it 'principle', since it was the only one I ever came across! I had worked for him every day for a year, including Christmas Day and Boxing Day, and had never received so much as a 'thank you'.

'. . . No excuse. No excuse,' cut in the inspector, in a frosty voice.

Mick then gave her the old farmer's stand-by – the 'old soldier' routine: 'Actually, I've not been very well, lately. I've got a bad heart, you know. I've even been thinking of retiring . . .'

'Good,' she cut in. 'The sooner the better, for my liking!' Spoken with real venom, this time. I winced.

Old Mick had done well not to get caught before now. During my first couple of weeks at the farm he had done the milking. I remember watching him, keen to learn the tricks of the trade, etc. I soon became disillusioned. He would never wash the cows' teats; did not have time to filter the milk, and if it was a cold day, would not even bother to cool it. I have even known him send off the churns to the dairy with some rather interesting looking brown bits floating on top of the warm milk. And all this time Mick was supposed to be training me.

'When I come back, next week . . . and I *will* come back . . .' she gave the word an ominous emphasis, '. . . I want to see the milking machines looking spotless, the milk cooler gleaming, the walls scrubbed, clean and whitewashed – and as for this floor, I want to be able to eat my breakfast off it! Otherwise . . .' she paused, did a passable impression of the smile on the face of a crocodile, then continued: '. . . you will lose your licence.'

'Can't I have a bit longer than a week,' pleaded Mick, wringing his hands. 'I'm a bit busy, you see.'

'No!' she replied, with a finality which precluded all further debate. 'I'll be back in seven days time. Early. 8.00 am. In time for breakfast, you might say,' she added, looking at the floor. At that, she turned on her heels, trudged off to her Ford Escort and sped away in a cloud of dust. Mick and I just stood and watched, wide-mouthed.

'Bloody hell!' exclaimed Mick, breaking the mood of the moment. He then went into his renowned swearing routine. The way he used those words . . . positively poetic. By now, of course, she was long gone, but it seemed to help him. To let off a bit more steam he threw his hat on the floor, and jumped on it a few times.

'What do you want?' he finally asked, gruffly.

'Can I buy some hay, Mick? I need some for my calves.'

'Oh, I don't know about that,' he said, ruefully. 'It's terribly expensive at the moment, you know – the price has shot right up, this last couple of months, due to the wet weather at haymaking time. Hay will be in short supply, this winter. . . .'

It was all I could do to stop yawning. This was the oldest story in the business. When you want to buy something from a farmer it is always about as rare as the dodo. Try to sell something, however, and there is a glut of them on the market . . . whatever it is!

'Oh, it's just that you've got about ten thousand bales of hay in your dutch barn,' I said, trying to sound casual. 'I thought you wouldn't miss one or two.'

'Oh, I don't know about that. . . .' He gave me part two of the saga.

'Look,' I said, 'the school is very short of cash. How about me sorting out your milking machine, fixing the cooler, and cleaning out the cowshed, in exchange for some hay?'

'Done!' he said, with what I felt was indecent haste. 'When can you start?'

'Four-thirty, this afternoon.'

'Why not now? No time like the present, you know!'

'True,' I said, 'but there is the small matter of my earning a living as a teacher.'

'Bah! Teachers! Who needs teachers,' exclaimed Mick. I was about to say that obviously he did, if only to clean out his cowshed . . . but thought better of it. It was, after all, a seller's market for hay.

On the way back to school I had time to reflect on what I had let myself in for. I had just started a new job; just started with the school farm, and now here I was taking on another job. What I needed was a 48-hour day; the thirty-six I was running on at present were just not enough. I was beginning to get cold feet – but I had given my word.

As I hurried back across the playground I could see that my form were sitting waiting for me to mark the register. I was just about to open the door to the classroom when, out of nowhere, the headmaster materialised by my side. Beats the heck out of me how he does it!

'Would you like me to mark the register for you?' he said sarcastically.

'No thanks . . . sorry I'm late,' I muttered.

'Remember, man, that marking the register is a legal obligation. What would the governors say at this laxness!'

I was sorely tempted to say that if he would clear off, I could get on with it. Discretion prevailed, however, so I just smiled and nodded politely.

After school I explained to the pupils that I had no time to do any weeding, then dived in the car and sped up to Mick's place. He had started milking, but that did not matter. I could work around him . . . and the cows. I found a bucket, a scraper and some scrubbing brushes. Mick said I would have to manage with just hot water, he could not afford detergent. I started on the wall at the back of the cows. It really was hard going. The muck and dirt were caked on hard, and I really had to soak it to get anywhere.

Once the milking was finished and the cows were let out I got to work on the top part of the walls. I used a brush to sweep down all the big cobwebs. Then I turned a hosepipe on the walls from top to bottom and left it to soak overnight. On the way out I placed a bale of hay in the boot of my car – something on account, as it were. It broke my heart to see his ten thousand bales. I would not have minded but he still only had a few animals. That much hay would last them a lifetime!

Next morning I did a further two hours of hard graft before going in to school. I went back after school, at 4.30 pm, and worked until quite late. All weekend, too, I worked on that cowshed, when I should have been planning lessons and preparing my school work. The tops of the walls were not too bad to clean; it was the bottom part. Even after extensive soaking it was hard work trying to shift the muck. Not only was I bringing off the paint, I was actually bringing off the plaster, too!

When I had finished the walls I started on the mangers. They were awful. Layers and layers of food were stuck on them, mixed in with hay seeds and all glued together with hardened saliva. There were even holes in the concrete mangers – with mice running in and out of them!

The following week I whitewashed the walls, cleaned the milking machines and sorted out the cooler. I did not have time to concrete up the holes in the mangers (much to the relief of the mice, I suspect) but Mick said he would shake some hay up in them, so that 'she who must be obeyed' would not notice. He never changed – always the easy way out. The day before she was due to make her auspicious return, the job was finished . . . and so was I. I had not only been burning the candle at both ends, I had been having a good go at the middle bit, too.

I gave Mick my record of hours worked. He looked up the agricultural rates of pay, and cross-referenced this with the average price of hay in the farming journals. He worked it out, then paid me in hay – minus my one bale 'advance'. That was it, mind you. Not one word of thanks; not one comment on how nice it looked.

By this time, Pinkie and Blackie had settled in well. Already, they were firm favourites with the pupils. I had made Clive my chief 'cow-hand' – to his great satisfaction. I just hoped the novelty would not wear off. I was conscious that I just was not spending enough time on the school farm, but with Mick's cowshed out of the way I could see my way clear at last.

Still, I could not resist popping up to Mick's place the next morning to see how he got on with the infamous Miss Smart. I arrived at ten minutes to eight.

'What's up? Can't you keep away?' asked Mick. He had finished the milking, and had actually remembered to swill out the shed. I noticed the hay in the mangers, covering the mouse holes. I wondered whether he was going to get away with that.

'Well, I just thought I'd pop and see what this woman reckoned to my cleaning job,' I replied.

'Huh! I've got a surprise for her, I can tell you.'

'What's that, then?' I asked.

'Ah . . . you just wait and see,' he said, cagily, with an evil grin on his face – a bit like an overgrown Cheshire cat.

At bang on eight o'clock the Ford Escort pulled into the farmyard, and Miss Smart got out. 'Good morning, gentlemen. Nice day. Now let's see what sort of job you've made of this.' She smiled the smile of someone who has seen it all before, and she spoke with that voice of chilling authority, like a spinsterly headmistress.

'Come on then!' she said. 'Let's get moving. It's 0800 hours, you know,' and with that she strode off across the yard, towards the cowshed. We just looked at each other, then ran to catch up with her, like a couple of obedient terriers.

As she entered the cowshed, she stopped dead in her tracks. The walls were so white they nearly dazzled you. After I had finished the cows had been reluctant to go back in. Creatures of habit, are cows, and they obviously thought this was not their cowshed. Miss Smart walked up and down checking the walls and looking at the floor, but without saying a word. Finally, she spoke: 'A vast improvement, Mr Hardy. I must say, I'm very pleased.'

Mick smiled that evil smile again, turned, and disappeared off towards the farmhouse. We watched as he went indoors. A minute later he reappeared – with a steaming frying pan in his hand. His wife had obviously been busy. The pan was hot, and the fat was sizzling away. Inside the pan, as he removed the lid, were two eggs, a fat rasher of bacon, fried bread, sausages, tomatoes and mushrooms. The aroma of the cooking wafted around us. It smelt superb.

'Come here,' he said, going into the cowshed. We followed, puzzled at what was going on. 'Now,' he said, 'we had a bargain. You wanted this floor so clean that you could eat your breakfast off it. Well . . . here goes.' And with that he tipped the lot onto the cowshed floor! 'There's your breakfast, now you keep your part of the bargain, and get stuck in.' He pushed a knife and fork into the bewildered Miss Smart's hands. 'There's toast and marmalade to follow, and coffee, of course!'

Miss Smart just stood there, dumbfounded. I could not help a sly snigger.

'Well,' she finally said, going quite red. 'I've met some tough, awkward old codgers in my time, but you, Mr Hardy, take the proverbial cake!' She flung down the knife and fork, turned, and marched off back to her car. She slammed the door and screeched out of the farm yard.

Mick was laughing so much I thought he was going to have a heart attack. 'Serves her right!' he laughed. 'Miss know-it-all Smart!' He looked at the food, still steaming, on the floor, and then looked at me. 'Seems a shame to waste it doesn't it, John? You can have it for 50p.' I said nothing. If I had offered the money he would have taken it.

Mick scraped up the food and threw it to one of his sows. She must have thought it was her birthday – though I was not at all sure that she should be tucking in to the pork sausage and the rasher of bacon with quite so much gusto.

From that time on Mick came under pretty close scrutiny from the farm inspectors in general . . . and Miss Smart in particular. They visited him at least twice as often as any other farm in the area, and he really had to stay on top of the job.

As for me, well, I stacked the hay at the school, in a nice, neat, square stack. I covered it with tin sheeting. It meant a lot to me, that hay, and I really begrudged using it. I had sweated blood for the stuff, and I hoped that Pinkie and Blackie appreciated it.

From Bike Shed to Pig-Pen

'WHERE HAVE you been until this time?' I asked Steven Wood, in my sternest voice. It was 2.30 in the afternoon and school started at 1.25; he was over an hour late.

'Sorry I'm late, Sir, but my Dad got burnt,' he replied, staring at the floor and with one of those hang-dog expressions which all too often afflict the face of the adolescent.

'I'm sorry,' I replied, now feeling somewhat guilty. 'Not seriously, I hope?'

'They don't mess about at the crematorium, Sir!' he said, raising his head and beaming all over his face. The class erupted. I thought I had memorised all the gems of wit and wisdom which new teachers get in class as part of the baptism of fire, but I was slipping.

It was my third week of full-time teaching, and by now I realised that some kind soul had certainly thrown me in the deep end with these fifteen-year-old lads.

They were a right bunch of misfits. Six out of the fifteen had criminal records, including Clive Gibson our calf-rearer. Raymond Huntingdon had a record as long as your arm. Though only just sixteen, he had already been convicted of breaking and entering. His partner in crime was Colin Fry – though it was Raymond who was the driving force in their partnership. Nicholas Galloway had stolen a car, and then had smashed up a dozen other vehicles trying to get it out of the Co-op car park. Neil Reed and Martin Towers specialised in shop-lifting, and Martin had even boasted to me, in front of the class, just how they had gone about stealing some watches. Steven Wood, the class comedian, quipped:

'He did time for that one, Sir!'

27

The other nine boys were 'clean', as yet – as far as the police were concerned, anyway. Though always in trouble at school, they were very much minor league material compared with their more illustrious compatriots of 5S3. Lawrence Bingham had a reading age of seven. Alan Neale was similarly blessed, but coupled this with something that amounted to a phobia about coming to school; he was always absent on some pretext or another. If brains were dynamite, he would not have had enough to blow his hat off. Steven Wood – the comedian – was an enormous fat boy – our school's answer to Bernard Manning.

Most of our pupils came from middle-class backgrounds, since the school is located in a nice part of town. However, there I was, a 'greenie teacher', lumbered with this lot. I taught the 'normal' pupils for science – but my rural studies group was this motley crew. Full of idealism, I was sure I was going to change all that and have a good cross-section of the school taking rural studies. The calves had been a good start and for many pupils this was their first experience with livestock. Getting some pigs was my next goal. I intended buying a couple of six-week-old weaner pigs and rearing them until they were about eighteen weeks old, selling them to customers as half-pigs for the freezer. That way I would cut out the 'middle-man' and pocket the full profit for the department.

Housing the pigs was my problem. I only had the one shed, now used for housing our calves, and there was certainly not enough room for two pigs as well.

I made a surreptitious reconnaissance round the school cycle sheds. There were three of these; two big, long sheds with open fronts, and one small shed about ten feet long by eight feet wide, with a large door on the front. One morning I watched the pupils putting their bikes into the sheds. They found it too much trouble to open the door of the small shed and nine times out of ten they would settle for the larger, open-fronted ones.

Interesting, I thought; that little shed would be ideal for my purposes. . . .

I took my rural studies renegades into my confidence, and explained about the small cycle shed. I would speak to the headmaster, I said, and see if we could move it to our department. It was made in six timber sections, all bolted together. At each end there was a window which opened, and it had a corrugated metal roof. Seven feet high in the front, sloping to six feet at the back, it would be an ideal home for my two pigs.

The kids liked the idea – a couple even became positively enthusiastic. Two calves – now two pigs; what would be next? An elephant, perhaps?

'Where are we going to put the shed?' asked Raymond.

'Not too far away from our mobile classroom,' I replied.

I walked outside, armed with a notebook and pencil, closely followed by the enthusiastic youngsters. We decided to place it at the rear of the classroom, a little to the right-hand side. I did not want it spoiling the view from the classroom windows. Though it was nothing to write home about at present, in my mind's eye I could picture the lawn, flowers and trees which one day would be there. The new shed would not detract from the view, but would be near enough to the classroom for easy feeding and cleaning. The site was level, and we had cleared it of weeds the week before.

'We cannot have a floor made of soil, because the pigs will dig into it with their noses,' I said. 'I wouldn't be surprised if they even got around to forming an escape committee and tunnelling their way out.'

'A load of readimix concrete is what we need,' announced Raymond.

'I agree,' I said, 'but we couldn't possibly afford a load, and I don't think we could really afford the sand and cement to do the job ourselves.'

'It would take a heck of a lot,' added Raymond, nodding pensively.

'We'll need some hardcore for the base,' chipped in Clive. 'There's a pile of hardcore over there. I'll smash it up into smaller pieces with a sledge-hammer.'

Great, thought I. He'll love that job – just up his street, smashing things.

'We haven't got a sledge-hammer,' I replied.

'I can get one!' said Clive.

'I bet you can. But I don't think the headmaster would appreciate being arrested for receiving stolen property.'

'Come on, Sir,' said Clive. 'Who said anything about stealing one?' The look on his face did nothing to allay my suspicions.

I rummaged through the pile of bricks and broken paving slabs. I had got most of it from the 'garden', in my first few days at school. We could now put it to good use, and I reckoned we might just have enough.

'If we dig out an area about six to eight inches deep, fill it up with the hardcore, then put a layer of sand on top and finally these broken slabs, it will make a great base,' I said. 'We can fill the cracks between the slabs with concrete and we'll have a good floor. It's got to be the cheapest way of doing it.'

'Brilliant!' exclaimed Steven. I was not going to argue with the boy.

Robert – one of the quieter boys – disappeared into the classroom and came out with two spades.

'He's going to use one in each hand,' quipped Steven. Robert smiled, handed a spade to Steven, and the boys got down to some hard digging. I came up with four pegs and marked out the site, knocking the pegs in with a half-brick since we did not possess a mallet. I ran string around the pegs, which marked out a site some one foot wider, each way, than the shed itself would be.

I had to hand it to the lads, they really worked at it. We continued through lunchtime and on into the evening until it got dark. Somehow, I had not got around to making that fateful trip to the headmaster's office and getting permission. Still, I was sure it was only a formality. . . . He was bound to agree.

We finished digging the next morning. With splendid forward planning, it then began to rain, and the whole thing filled up with water. I do not know about a pig-pen, it would have made a great fish pond. After school the boys could not wait for the water to drain away and insisted on bailing it out with buckets. The hardcore was then thrown in with great abandon on the part of all the participants – myself included.

The next morning, Clive turned up brandishing a very impressive sledge-hammer. I omitted to ask where it had come from; better not to know such things. I just hoped the headmaster had not seen him; it is not the sort of tool you can hide in your satchel. Clive smashed up the hardcore in double quick time. At the end of my lesson, he was all for walking off to his next lesson, sledge-hammer on his shoulder, like one of Snow White's gnomes.

'I think you ought to leave that hammer here,' I suggested.

'It might get stolen!' he replied.

'Who would want to steal a sledge-hammer?'

'I would,' replied Clive, in all seriousness.

'Put it in the classroom; I'll keep an eye on it,' I conceded.

'OK, Sir . . . but it's a pity. I've got Mr Harris for next period. If he gets too bossy, I could . . .'

He had a way with words, young Clive.

I bribed the caretaker, and after the obligatory moans which seem to come with the territory for all of those of the janitorial profession, he agreed to give me the ashes out of the school boiler. These I put on top of the hardcore base. They settled between the pieces of hardcore and gave me a nice level surface which I packed down with a borrowed garden roller.

The sand and cement I bought – with my own money – from a local builder's yard. It was cheaper if you collected it yourself, and they had quite a chuckle at my expense when they loaded it on to the back of my car. We were then ready to begin the work of laying the crazy-paving floor.

I put half an inch of sand down first. Then, starting at one corner and using a spirit level, I laid each broken slab

31

on a continuous layer of concrete. It was like some elaborate jigsaw puzzle, but worked out well. The boys again worked really hard mixing up the sand and cement. In next to no time we had the floor laid and the cracks filled with concrete. We made the floor slope slightly, for ease of cleaning.

'A good job done,' pronounced Steven, 'but I know someone who could have done it even better.'

'Who's that?' I asked.

'A bloke who lives in an asylum,' he replied.

'I don't get it.'

'A psychopath, Sir!' The lads all fell about.

'Have you spoken to the headmaster yet, Sir?' asked Clive.

'Er . . . I'm going to see him about it tomorrow,' I said – the first thing that came into my mind. Oh boy, ambushed! Still, I had been putting it off for far too long.

The next day I approached the headmaster in the staffroom, catching him just as he was looking for the sugar to put in his tea.

'Er, Headmaster . . . do you think I could have that bicycle shed on the playground, you know, the small one, with the door on the front . . . please?'

'Certainly not,' he said with remarkable brevity, still searching in a somewhat preoccupied fashion for the sugar bowl on the table.

'But . . . er . . . I could really use it. I need a place to keep the pigs – the pigs we'll soon be getting, that is.'

'And what would the county council think of that? Me giving you a perfectly good bicycle shed – a shed they have paid for to house cycles, not dirty pigs!' The search for the elusive sugar bowl continued. 'If it was in poor condition, or if it was falling to pieces, it would be different. As it is, I just couldn't justify it. What would the county council think!' At this moment, one of the other teachers walked over to the table, returning the sugar bowl. The headmaster gave him one of his best, withering, 'black mark' looks. The poor man retreated, mumbling apologies.

This quite put me off my stride. I wanted to tell him that pigs are not really dirty; that they wallow in mud to keep cool, but on the whole they are very clean. I wanted to tell him, too, of the hard work my rural studies lads had done in constructing the base. My aimless effort to organise my thoughts came to nothing, though, as the needlework teacher elbowed her way in at this point. She wanted some new curtains for her classroom. The head-master – now all smiles – said he would be more than happy for her to go ahead with this – important to encourage the pupils – conducive surroundings for the work. Then the bell went for the end of break. I was left speechless and disappointed. All that work. How was I going to break it to the boys? I just did not have the money to buy a new shed, and did not think we had much chance of picking up a second-hand one for the five pounds we had in our department's fund.

After lunch I got the lads together and broke the news to them. They were really disappointed. I had given them some homework to find out all about pigs; now they did not want to do that. I felt terrible – as though I had let them down. I had failed to deliver on my part of the deal.

I spent a depressed evening and a restless night still thinking about the matter. I drove to school the next day, still preoccupied, but with no answer as to how to solve the problem. I went through the morning on 'automatic pilot', with all the enthusiasm gone out of me, and dreading my afternoon period with 5S3. Over my cup of tea, at break, I continued to be withdrawn, looking for solutions where none existed.

An all-too-familiar voice cut through my reflections – the stern voice of the headmaster.

'I looked at that bicycle shed this morning. The damned thing is a shambles – a real eye-sore! Take the horrible thing out of the way, man. I've never seen such a mess. Half the front is missing, and there's no back to it. Look, shift it, or we'll have the neighbours complaining.'

I stood, mouth gaping, just looking at him.

'Pull yourself together, man. I know that you are only a young teacher, in your probationary year, but you must learn to stand up for yourself. When I told you it was in good condition, yesterday, you should have spoken up for yourself. If you still want the shed, take it. If not, I'll have the caretaker dismantle what's left of it and burn it.'

With that he turned and walked towards the staffroom door.

'Er . . . Er . . . yes . . . thank you . . .' I stammered, gathering my scattered wits.

I ran outside to the cycle sheds. I could not believe my eyes. Where, just yesterday, had been a perfectly presentable shed there now stood this awful ruin, with half the front missing, and no back. It looked as though a bunch of vandals had . . .

At lunchtime I found the lads on the playground. I told them the latest news, and also that certain parts of the shed were now missing, and we would need to patch it up. They seemed remarkably unconcerned. Clive just smiled. We arranged to move the shed to its new position that evening, after school.

It took a bit of dismantling, since the nuts and bolts were all rusted. I used my trusty helper – a big hammer, the farmer's favourite friend – and we soon had it down. The lads made light work of carrying the panels to the new site, and we soon had it reassembled – at least as much of it as we now had. I got out my camera and took a picture of our very first farm building on our school farm.

'From little acorns, mighty oak trees grow,' I philosophised.

The boys just grinned. Five minutes later, as if by magic, the missing pieces had mysteriously reappeared, and were firmly in place.

'Not quite an oak tree, Sir,' grinned Clive, 'but it's got to be an improvement, hasn't it?'

So that is the story of how we came by our illustrious pig-pen. The headmaster even complimented me on the repairs we had made on the old shed. 'Looks almost presentable now,' he said.

I suppose in this life we all have to learn to use our skills. The rogues of 5S3 had certainly done that. It was just that their skills and talents lay in what might be termed slightly unconventional areas.

Two days later I bought our first two weaner pigs from a local farmer. They arrived, pink and plump, and we put them in our new accommodation. We fed them on pig meal – a balanced ration designed to help them grow as quickly as possible from 'weaners' to 'porkers'.

Our farm was up and running.

Duck Pond Capers

'PLEASE SIR, can we have a duck pond?'

Robert, the boy asking the question, had pleading in his eyes. He went on: 'I feel sorry for our six ducks with only an old sink to swim in. As soon as we fill it they empty it again.'

I could not disagree. The ducks all made a bee-line for the water, leapt about like wild things, and splashed it everywhere.

I had bought the ducks very cheaply from a local farmer. As usual, I had pleaded poverty. The farmer had taken pity on us, and the ducks were ours for less than half the market price. We had an Aylesbury drake and duck called Jeremy and Jemima – names courtesy of a certain Beatrix Potter. The Aylesbury breed are reckoned to be about the best for 'duck dinners', and it was our intention to breed from this pair, rearing all the young for slaughter. The other four ducks were Khaki Campbells. Since none of us could tell one from the other – they are smaller and brown in colour – they remained nameless. Khaki Campbells are fantastic egg layers, producing more eggs per bird in a year, on average, than a battery hen, although duck eggs are much more difficult to sell than hen eggs – something of an acquired taste, in fact. Some people even worry about food poisoning.

'That's a good idea, Robert. A duck pond would be great,' I replied enthusiastically. 'I don't think the lads could dig it, though; I suppose I'll have to hire a JCB.'

There was a chorus of 'No, Sir!' and 'No – we'll dig it!' from the fifteen boys in the class. A nice bit of reverse psychology, that; tell them they cannot do something, and it suddenly becomes a challenge. I had wanted a duck pond all along, but now it was 'their idea', and they would take much more interest in it.

The lads were all in favour of getting started right away. It was Friday morning, and raining heavily. The kids hated written work and classroom learning, and were never happier than when they had their sleeves rolled up, getting down to some 'real' work. Given half a chance, they would have begun digging there and then, right outside the classroom door.

I was secretly pleased that it was raining. I was to have given a lesson on flowering plants, but changed my mind; we would talk about ponds: planning and construction. I did not tell the lads that I had never dug a pond before. I had read about it in the past. I knew enough for about an hour's work.

The first thing to resolve was just where it would go. I wanted it so that it could be seen from the classroom window. I also wanted it on level ground, away from trees, so that I would not have to spend all my time fishing leaves out of it. The ideal spot was some thirty metres from the classroom windows.

'What do we do with the soil?' asked the enthusiastic Robert.

'Dig another hole to put it in,' quipped Steven, as ready as ever with the quick response.

I had always wanted a rockery, planted with heathers and dwarf conifers. We could use the topsoil for that, but the clay would have to be dumped.

The rain continued to beat on the windows.

'It's a pity it's not dug,' said Robert. 'We wouldn't need a hosepipe to fill it; just look at the weather.'

'What size pool do we need?' I asked. I received every answer from a tin bath sunk in the ground to something bordering on one of the Canadian Great Lakes – with accompanying sailing, powerboat and trawler fishing facilities. We compromised. It would be fifteen feet long, ten feet wide and three feet deep.

'Can we have some fish in it as well, please Sir?'

'Yes . . . for about two minutes.' The boys laughed. I explained that we would do better to construct a separate fish pond at a later date, since ducks will eat the fish and wreck the water plants, searching for insects amongst the roots. We agreed to make the pool look as natural as possible – not the rectangular bright blue type. But how would we retain the water?'

'Concrete would be best,' I said, 'but we just cannot afford it.'

'My dad bought a glass fibre pool; it was easy to put into the ground,' contributed Michael.

'They're too small,' I said, 'and besides, they're very expensive.'

'Can't we just dig down to the clay and let the clay hold the water?' queried Robert.

'That does work in some areas, but I don't think we'll get away with it here, because of the nature of the soil. If we had a dry spell I think we would find the pond would dry up.' I had seen some flexible liners in pet shops, made out of butyl rubber or laminated PVC. I guessed these would also be too expensive.

'Polythene sheeting is the cheapest,' I announced.

'My dad can get that from work,' exclaimed Robert.

The class looked very pleased. Robert had come up with the original idea, and now he was going to supply the lining material for free. I agreed that he should ask his father, but at the back of my mind had some reservations. I just hoped that the materials would be acquired legitimately.

Robert was usually a good lad, but about a year before he

had been in trouble with the headmaster for stealing some pencils out of the English teacher's desk. The headmaster had 'invited' Robert's father to school, and he and Mr Harris, the English teacher, had outlined the problem. At the end of a somewhat lengthy discussion, Robert's father had simply commented:

'I can't understand why he needs to steal pencils from school. I can bring him plenty from work!'

My reservations went rumbling round my brain for the rest of the lesson. What had I agreed to? The reverie was interrupted by the bell. Like schoolboys everywhere, my class reacted like greyhounds to a hare, grabbing books and rulers, stuffing them into satchels and making a run for the door.

'Hold it, you lot!' I yelled over the din. Grabbing a pile of graph paper I gave each pupil a piece. 'For homework, design and draw the pond to scale.'

A week later I gathered in the homework and sifted through it for the best design. I came up with a rather nice kidney-shaped pool designed by Mark, who was talented at technical drawing. Armed with a pointed stick and enthusiastically pursued by my tribe of faithful followers I walked round to the site. We measured the area, and then I used the stick to draw out the shape of the pool in the soft topsoil. I felt a bit like Colonel Custer, briefing the troops before the Battle of the Little Bighorn . . . though I hoped the outcome would be rather more successful.

Then the digging began. The topsoil was easy to transport in our wheelbarrow to a site some twenty metres away which I had earmarked for our rockery. One of the lads borrowed a second wheelbarrow and another spade, and the work went on apace.

The next day – Saturday – it rained, and work came to a standstill. Sunday was fine, however, and we were ready to resume work at Monday lunchtime. We were now down to the clay which we put on one side for later disposal. We dug a level floor and shaped the sides of the pond so that they were gently sloping. I checked it with a spirit level, and we made some adjustments until we got it just right. Then we checked the bottom and sides for any protruding stones which might play havoc with our lining.

We really needed to put a layer of sand down next as a seating for the polythene liner. I had noticed that some builders were working in the area, and so pulled off a 'trade', swapping a dozen new-laid eggs for a half a dozen barrow-loads of sand. All we needed now was the lining.

Robert brought it to school the next day, all neatly folded and obviously brand new. We put it into position, and carefully filled the pool, using a long hosepipe I had borrowed from a local farmer, since our nearest tap was some hundred metres away. It looked fine. We trimmed the edge of the lining to leave a foot or so all round, and then put some broken slabs on top of this, hoping to concrete them into position at a later date. We were all ready for the ducks. I toyed, fleetingly, with the idea of inviting the headmaster to come and crack a bottle of lemonade over the pond, and launch the first duck . . . but did not really think that was his style.

At 9.00 am the next morning we let loose the un-suspecting creatures and herded them towards the pond. The leader let out a squawk and went for the water like a bat out of hell, with the rest in hot pursuit. They plunged in and went tearing round like mad things, splashing and quacking and making a real racket. We went in to assembly, feeling proud of ourselves.

I returned later in the morning. All was not well, I sensed. I could hear the odd quack as I approached . . . but there was not a duck in sight. As I got nearer I could see the problem. The ducks were still there – but now somewhat more subdued, floating dejectedly on the six inches of water still remaining in the pond. The plastic sheeting was all ripped to bits. Only then did I remember that ducks had little claws on their webbed feet. These had done the lining no good at all.

The lads were shattered.

'But surely, you must have realised . . .' began Robert. He was right; I should have done.

That evening I was propping up the bar at the Black Horse, the venue for our regular Young Farmers' meetings. I got talking to a fellow I knew slightly, and told him of our disaster with the ducks.

'How much concrete would you need to make a permanent job?' he asked.

'Oh, I'd be willing to make the pond smaller,' I said. 'About five or six barrow loads would do the trick, I think.'

'Leave it to me,' he said, pulling deep on his pint.

He introduced himself as George Green, and told me he was 'in concrete'. Sounded a bit messy . . . but I was in the market for all the help I could get. He told me he would arrange for one of his drivers to drop me off a load of ready-mixed concrete free of charge. I could not believe my luck; this was the first time I had ever really spoken to the man, and he was offering me something for nothing. I know that I am good at a sob story, but that was pretty good, even for me. I bought him a pint, and drove home on 'cloud nine'.

I took out the torn lining the next day, just to be ready. I kept the ducks penned up, having filled their old sink once more. They gave me looks of absolute disgust.

At 9.30 am I came out of assembly to find a huge concrete mixer lorry coming roaring across the playground. Stopping abruptly, the driver leaned out of his cab, plaid cap jauntily pulled down over his eyes and the inevitable Woodbine drooping from his lips.

'Eh, mate, where do yer want this lot tippin'?' he asked in his best Birmingham accent.

'Oh . . . er . . . tip it here, outside the classroom, by the door, please.'

Taking me at my word, he did just that. He revved up, backed the lorry right up to the classroom and tilted the mixer to spew out its load slap bang in front of the door. One barrow-load of concrete . . . two . . . three . . . four . . . nine . . . twelve . . . sixteen! I lost count. The full load was dumped unceremoniously up against the building. It stood

41

four feet high, completely blocking the door. I could not even see the handle, and had a vision of the wet and sticky stuff oozing into the classroom.

'Er . . . er . . . I only expected about five or six barrow loads,' I stammered.

'No point messing about with half-measures,' he said.

I did not think I would tell him that I would have been more than happy with a 'half-measure'.

'How much do I owe you?' I ventured somewhat tentatively, thinking of the dent this would make in my meagre farm fund.

'Nowt!' he replied.

'Nowt . . . er . . . nothing?' I queried.

'Nope. The boss says I was to bring you a load and a load I've brought.'

There was no arguing with that. The wet and glistening pile was all too evident – a concrete reminder, as it were. He climbed back into the cab and shot off down the drive.

By now a small crowd had gathered, looking in stunned admiration at this rather remarkable piece of modern art propping up my classroom door. It dawned upon me that this was my group for the next lesson period. There was just one small problem, however.

'No writing today,' I announced. The lads cheered. I wrote a quick note to be taken to the deputy head, explaining the situation and asking if I could keep the pupils beyond their scheduled double period of eighty minutes. I added, too, that I would really appreciate it if someone could cover me for my two science lessons after break. Not that I am against science, as such – but a load of rapidly setting concrete does take precedence in my book – particularly when it is leaning up against my classroom door! A thought suddenly flashed into my mind: what would have happened if there had been anyone in the classroom at the time . . . trapped? How would I have broken that to the headmaster? I shuddered, and turned my thoughts to more practical things.

About ten minutes later my 'runner' returned, puffing

and panting. He handed me a scribbled reply to my note. Great! The deputy head had come up trumps, sorting out the necessary arrangements. There was only one fly in the ointment – old Harris. Mr Harris, the English teacher, was 'not happy' about the pupils missing his English lesson. I reckon the boys would rather go to the dentist than sit through one of his English lessons – but he was a real 'academic', and he and I did not exactly see eye to eye, to say the very least.

I hurtled off to the English room and cornered Harris.

The only thing to do was to 'crawl' – much as it went against the grain. I begged, pleaded, got my violin out and gave him a chorus of 'Hearts and Flowers' ... and he finally agreed. I made a mental note to 'get even'.

My main problem was that I was just not geared up for the job. All I had was one small wheelbarrow – not the real 'farming' type, but the sort that genteel English ladies of advanced years might use to tidy up a window box. I had one shovel ... and a very small trowel. The wheel had dropped off the borrowed second barrow.

By now the pile of concrete was doing a passable impression of the Matterhorn. It seemed to be getting bigger and bigger all the time. Still, nothing for it but to get started.

The lads were great. They began shifting the concrete into the barrow, wheeling the barrow gingerly down to the pond and tipping the concrete in. I concentrated on laying it. The trouble was that I had just too much. I started with a four-inch concrete lining but the barrow-loads kept coming and coming. I added another four inches, but still the concrete came, and I hated to waste it. I had visions of a pond which would be atom-bomb proof ... and two inches deep. Every time I looked up that barrow was heading towards me, stacked high with even more concrete!

I asked Joe, one of our neighbours, if he could use some. He agreed, saying that he would make a concrete base for his dustbin. Another neighbour took three barrow-loads to make a garden path, and we even made a concrete surround to the pond.

By now it was 1.25 pm, time to mark the afternoon register and start teaching again. We had missed both break and lunchtime in our haste to get the job done.

In the afternoon we were honoured by a visit from the headmaster. The deputy head had no doubt told him of the 'fun and games' we were having, and he had torn himself away from his precious paperwork to cast an eagle eye over the proceedings. I showed him our marvellous new pond, with an obvious pride.

'Huh. And where did you get the money from for that?' he said, gesturing in the direction of this eighth wonder of the world.

Since I had been seeking funds from him just a couple of days before I had to admit it was not an unreasonable question.

'I met the director of a local concreting firm at the pu . . . er . . . Young Farmers' meeting, the other night, and he kindly agreed to donate a load of concrete to the school.'

The headmaster raised his eyebrows and smiled, albeit slightly. He nodded, appreciatively. 'We must send him a suitable thankyou note. Only right, you know, man.' He went off, mumbling to himself.

The next Thursday I was again at the Young Farmers' meeting. In came George Green.

'I was hoping to see you,' I said. 'Let me buy you a pint.'

He looked pleased.

'I really must thank you for that concrete. I only expected five or six barrow-loads, not a full load. It really was most generous of you.'

'My pleasure,' he said, smiling broadly, and then taking a long pull on his pint of best bitter.

'The headmaster is writing to your firm to express our thanks,' I added.

I thought he was going to choke. He spluttered on his beer, almost dropped his glass, and turned a funny colour.

'What!' he exclaimed. 'You're kidding . . . aren't you?'

'Why . . . what's the problem?' I asked innocently.

'Well, you fool, I don't own the firm, just manage it. That concrete came off the back of a lorry in more ways than one.'

Now it was my turn to have the proverbial heart attack. The colour drained from my cheeks as the implications of what he was saying sank in. He continued.

'The firm builds motorway bridges. Put it this way, bridge number 22 has now got just 299 lorry loads of concrete in it, rather than 300 – get my meaning?'

I got his meaning, all right – though I did not think it

would go down too well with my friend the headmaster.

'I'm pretty sure the letter hasn't gone out yet,' I said, somewhat pathetically.

'Well, get in there, lad, and make sure it doesn't!' Bribe the secretary, steal the thing . . . whatever it takes.'

I apologised three times, drank the remains of my pint in one gulp, and headed for the door.

I am not going to say exactly how the deed was done . . . but put it this way, I owe the secretary one.

A fortnight later we filled the pond and launched the ducks once more. Whoever came up with that expression, 'like ducks to water', certainly knew what he was talking about. At first, they seemed a bit 'reserved' – difficult for a duck – but I suppose it is a case of 'once bitten . . .'. This time, though, there were no problems.

You know, every time I travel down the motorway I think about our duck pond and that missing load of concrete. I am especially careful going under bridge 22 – usually take a good run at it, and get through as quickly as I can.

As for our duck pond, it is probably the only one in Britain built to motorway specifications!

Roast Pork

OUR TWO pigs were fattening well in their converted bicycle shed but were a little cramped for room. A Mr Ashley, a parent of a girl in the fourth year, had been elected on to the school Parent Teachers Association. He was a builder and he offered to help the school in any way he could; however, I bet he could have eaten his words as I jumped at this offer. I explained that we desperately needed some brick buildings to house livestock. Brick buildings are easier to maintain than wooden ones and they are also easier to keep clean.

I really wanted a large building: it would stand on the edge of the playground at the end of the mobile classroom. I had space for one twenty-five feet by sixteen feet. Mr Ashley thought this would be really too large a task for him and so offered to construct something garage size – sixteen feet by eight feet. I compromised and was very grateful.

Plans were passed, and Mr Ashley provided the bricks and his bricklaying skills free of charge. Volunteer pupils and I did the labouring; we bought sand, cement, timber for the rafters, and I was lucky enough to buy a couple of second-hand window frames and some roofing sheets very cheaply at a local farm sale. Mr Ashley was indeed a true professional, and the whole thing took only three weekends to build. We put a dividing wall down the centre of the building which gave us two pens eight feet square. We would house pigs in one side and calves the other.

The building cost us £110.00 to build. I used all of our farm profits, £59.00, which meant finding another £51.00. I donated £10.00 and at the same time the school PTA organised an Autumn Fayre, profits from which were well into the hundreds. At the PTA committee meeting Mr Ashley suggested clearing the rural studies department's debt, and it was unanimously decided that we should receive the £41.00. I rewarded Mr Ashley with our customary currency – a dozen new-laid eggs. He was pleased to do the job for us, but he did say that when we could afford to extend the building we ought to find another builder because, rightly so, he had done his bit.

Rather than sell our pigs to a butcher I had decided to look for four potential customers, people who might want to buy half a pig for their freezer. In no time at all I had found two staff members and two parents who said they were interested. I rang up half a dozen freezer centres to get an average price – and then added two pence a pound. Well, I thought, it was still a pretty good deal . . . and they were not short of money! Building up the department was every-thing, and every penny counted.

I was rapidly establishing the reputation of being a 'hard businessman' . . . to my face, that is; behind my back I was 'a tight-fisted scrounger', someone who would sell his granny for two pence. Still, needs must, when the devil drives.

Our two noisy little weaners were growing at a tremendous rate. They ought to have done, on what it was costing us. They were being fed twice daily, as well as being provided with water and a good bed of straw. Quite a life.

At eighteen weeks old they were getting really enormous, and were ready for slaughter. I was not sure just how this was going to go down with the pupils. These would be the first of our animals to make the proverbial one-way journey. Pupils were told, every week, not to get too attached to them, since they were farm animals, not pets, and would eventually end up on somebody's table. We had purposely bought some ducks and some rabbits for them to keep as pets, and had agreed not to get rid of these.

In any case, at eighteen weeks, they were no longer the cute little piglets of old, but big, boisterous beasties – with but one thought . . . for their bellies! They were taking a lot of looking after now, and the regular task of cleaning them out was becoming more and more burdensome for the pupils assigned to the task. Besides, once we had sold these two, I kept saying, we could buy some more little ones. I seemed to be winning.

The small matter of transport to the abattoir was something I had overlooked. I had no tow-bar on my car, so it was no use trying to borrow a trailer on its own. I needed to borrow a car and trailer or a van. I telephoned all my possible contacts, but drew a blank.

In desperation I rang a specialist firm of livestock transporters. Sure, they said, they could do it; the only problem was that the cost would be more than my profit on the sale. So I made my excuses and put the phone down. Back to the drawing board.

The annoying thing was that the abattoir was only about three miles away. I had a fleeting vision of driving the pigs through the streets of the town, at the dead of night . . . but sanity soon prevailed. How on earth could I solve the problem?

After the Young Farmers' meeting that Thursday evening I stood at the bar and poured out all my troubles to one of my friends. Stan, it appeared, owned two vehicles – a car and a mini-van. 'The mini-van is the wife's pride and joy,' he said. 'She calls it "min", and lavishes care and attention on it. Still . . . I might be able to help. . . .'

I quickly sank the rest of my pint, and ordered a refill for the both of us. I handed him the freshly pulled and still foaming drink. 'And . . . er . . . how do you think you might be able to help then?' I said, trying to sound as casual as I could.

'Well, the wife thinks the world of that little van, so we must carry out this whole delicate operation without her knowing,' said Stan, gulping his pint and giving me a knowing wink. He had another couple of deep swallows, and carried on. 'Alison – that's the wife – doesn't use the van for work. She gets a lift to and from the shop, so the van's at home all day . . . and she doesn't get in until about ten past five.'

My mind was racing now. 'It's difficult for me to get out of lessons, so the best time for me would be about 3.45, when school finishes for the day.'

'Could we be sure to get it back for ten past five?' asked Stan.

'No problem,' said I . . . with my fingers crossed behind my back. 'Five minutes to load the pigs; ten minutes travelling to the abattoir; five minutes unloading, and then we can allow half an hour to get back and clean the van out.' Stan spluttered into his beer. 'Not that I'm expecting any mess,' I added reassuringly, and with the biggest smile I could muster . . . which was not much, at that precise moment.

'What does that add up to, then?'

'I make it fifty minutes, so we'd be back and finished by a quarter to five at the latest. Like I say, no problem.'

'Then that's settled,' said the smiling Stan. 'But I'll have to drive, because it's not insured for anyone else.'

'Great!' I said. 'Is next Monday OK for you?' Stan nodded, and I felt as though all the worries in the world had suddenly been lifted from my shoulders. Nothing to it, this farming lark, I thought, and took another pull on my pint.

Monday arrived, and I felt confident. I had let my fifth-year class go a few minutes early, so that I could be out at the pig-pen in plenty of time. I thought through the arrangements. I had telephoned the abattoir and told them I would be there at about four o'clock. The pigs would be cut into joints, and I would pick them up at Wednesday lunchtime. Sounded good.

Stan arrived on time, tearing into the playground in his little van, and screeching to a halt. I motioned to him to reverse back to the pen, and he did a lightning three-point turn, crashing every gear en route, and backed up to the pig-pen at an alarming rate, just braking in time.

'Does your wife know you drive her little "min" like this?' I asked.

'No way! She'd kill me if she did,' said the grinning Stan, clearly enjoying himself.

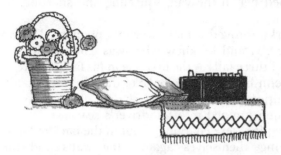

I looked inside. It was a real lady's vehicle – clean and tidy and smelling sweet and perfumed. It looked more like a sitting room on wheels, and it took us a few minutes to take out the carpet, the cushion and even a basket of dried flowers artfully arranged. In the back was a car battery. Funny that, I would not have thought she would have let him keep that there. Still, out it came.

I broke the strings on a bale of straw and put plenty of straw in the back. That should stop any 'accidents', I thought. Stan asked if I had a board or some wire we could string across behind the seats to keep the pigs in the back. I do not think Stan liked pigs all that much. I went back into the department and found a couple of boards, but they were not quite large enough. Suddenly I remembered some wire grids I had seen in the third-year cloakrooms. One of those would do nicely. I ran up the cloakroom, unscrewed one of the grids, and sneaked back out without anyone – that is, the headmaster – seeing me.

Stan was impatiently looking at his watch. 'Get a move on,' he said. I put the wire grid in the van. It fitted perfectly. We propped it up at the bottom with a concrete block, and put back the battery to wedge it at the other end. The top we tied with bale string. Stan gave it a shake. 'That's firm enough,' he said. 'Let's get the show on the road.'

We opened the pig-pen door and made a grab for 'Pinky', the smaller of the two. With the element of surprise in our favour, we quickly managed to pick her up between us and dumped her in the van, squealing and snorting. So far so good.

'Perky' proved a more worthy opponent. He was much bigger . . . and he knew what was coming. Still, after the 'best of three falls' – the first one in his favour – we had him, and soon he was in the back of the van, too. Stan took the precaution of tying up the back door of the van with string, and then jumped into the driver's seat.

The pigs were charging about in the back of the van, and throwing themselves against the walls and the door. 'They're denting the sides,' observed Stan, with a slight tremor in his voice which bordered on outright fear. 'Let's get the hell out of here!'

He revved up the van, and we shot off.

I do not think Stan had had too much experience at livestock transportation. Every time he braked – which was often – the two pigs came crashing into the wire grid, pushing it into our necks and backs. Stan raced out of the school drive, and took the first corner at about sixty. It was a right-hander, and my door flew open. Instinctively I reached out to grab the handle and close it. The road – and my life to date – were flashing past me as I tried to steady myself. 'You're not leaving us, are you?' said Stan, in a very cool and collected way. He accelerated again, and we sped on.

Then it hit me. Three electric shocks; one after another. At first I thought I had just imagined it – something to do with almost falling to my death, perhaps. Suddenly Stan sat bolt upright. 'I've just had an electric shock,' he screamed. 'You're lucky; I've had three,' I replied.

I glanced behind me and could immediately see the problem. The metal grid was actually touching the terminal of the battery, creating a short circuit. Suddenly, a spark shot off the battery and landed in the straw. Within seconds the straw in the back of the van was on fire.

We were travelling up a hill at the time, and Stan slammed to a halt outside a school. Children were spilling out of the gates, on their way home. We jumped out and raced to the back of the van, Stan taking off his coat on the way. I was pulling at the doors – tied together by the string, of course – and wishing that I had paid more attention to my old scoutmaster on the subject of knots, since neither of us had a penknife.

By this time smoke was pouring out of the open windows at the front of the van, and a crowd had started to gather. The pupils thought it was great fun, and some older students who had been passing shouted something about smokey bacon.

Finally the string gave way and the doors swung open. Black smoke came billowing from inside, and flames were whipping around the pigs' feet and legs. Stan dived in – and I slammed the door shut behind him, thinking to prevent the pigs charging out and into the traffic. The honking of car horns caused me to look around, and I could see that our parking had been a little less than helpful, since we, and the school bus parked opposite, were now totally blocking the road. An impressive looking traffic jam was already building up.

The pupils on the school bus entered into the spirit of the thing, shouting helpful remarks, mainly of the Anglo-Saxon variety. The pigs were squealing; Stan was bellowing at them – and smoke was continuing to billow from the windows. Leaning against the back doors of the van I had that all too familiar sinking feeling in the pit of my stomach. . . .

After what seemed like an eternity, but which was, in fact, no more than a minute or so, Stan banged on the back doors of the van and shouted for me to open them, which I did and he clambered out.

'Have you been burnt?' I yelled.

'No, I'm all right – but the pigs were frightened and kept getting in the way when I was trying to beat out the flames.'

I realised that we were holding up the traffic, but just had to look quickly into the back of the van. The sight that met my eyes was incredible. Standing wide-eyed and looking slightly embarrassed, so it seemed, were my two fat, black pigs. Black? Their entire coats were blackened with smoke,

apart, that is, for a small white ring around their eyes. Otherwise they were unharmed. The chorus of car horns brought me back from my wide-eyed wonderment and we fastened up the back of the van, jumped in, and drove off past the crowd of onlookers.

We sat in silence, Stan staring fixedly through the windscreen, and gripping the wheel tightly. I wondered if the police had been called – or even the fire brigade – and I was trying to figure out how I would talk my way out of this one.

'Lucky the van didn't blow up,' said Stan, breaking the tense silence, 'there's a full tank of petrol.'

I nodded nervously. 'That could have been very nasty,' I replied. 'Still, it's over now . . .' My words carried little conviction.

We turned into the abattoir yard, booked in at the office, and were given instructions on how we were to unload. We got to the unloading bay to find that a large wagon had beaten us to it, and two hundred lambs – on two decks –

needed to be unloaded. The wait cost us fifteen precious minutes.

Finally the wagon pulled over to one side, and Stan backed the van into position. A rough looking character – the sort of guy who plays the villain in an old western movie – came over to give us a hand. I undid the back of the van to reveal our two blackened pigs.

'Wh . . . what the hell are they?' stammered the somewhat shattered worker.

'Er . . . the van caught fire,' I said.

'You're joking!'

'No . . . no, it's true,' I insisted.

'It's the first time I've seen anyone try to cook their pork before it's dead,' he roared, now beaming all over his wrinkled face.

Stan and I managed a smile – quite an achievement, all things considered – and we quickly unloaded the pigs. They seemed quite keen to get out of the van. I was given a receipt, and confirmed the time for picking up the meat. We got back into the van, and both gingerly looked over our shoulders at its somewhat modified interior.

The aroma of perfume had definitely gone, to be replaced by an all-pervading smell of smoke. The floor was covered in burnt straw, ashes and pig muck. The sides of the van – once a delightful pale pink colour – were now black and had some rather interesting looking bulges in the metal work, and the roof was covered in soot. We looked at each other, but said nothing. Stan again crunched the gears, and hit the accelerator – hard.

It was five o'clock by the time we tore back into Stan's drive. Jumping out, he yelled, 'We've got ten minutes. Let's get a move on.' He disappeared into the garden shed and came out brandishing a garden fork, shovel and brush. 'You muck out the van, and pile it at the back. I'll put it on the roses . . . might as well get something out of this.' Fine sense of humour, Stan – and very practical, I thought. He was frantically pushing away at the sides of the van to try to restore them to something like their former shape.

I cleared out the mess from the floor: Stan was now scrubbing away at the sides and roof with a wet cloth. We were making progress, but the main problem was that the floor of the van had ridges in it, and the brush was just wiping over the top of these, leaving lots of muck in the bottom. 'I've got an idea,' shrieked Stan, darting off in the direction of the house. He re-emerged a moment or two later with a vacuum cleaner in his hands, and yards and yards of extension cable.

'It looks brand new,' I commented.

'It is,' he said, 'we only bought it a fortnight ago. He plugged it into the extension, and proceeded to vacuum out the mess, using the large flexible hose. The muck and straw slurped its way up the tube as the motor fought bravely to cope with it. The constant high-pitch whining of the motor soon gave way to an occasional hiccup; the motor began cutting out intermittently – then stopped altogether. We looked at each other. 'You haven't pulled the plug out, have you?' I ventured. He raced back into the house, and returned with a slightly puzzled look on his face.

'No. The plug's still in properly; it must have packed in.' He undid the hose and peered down it. 'It's blocked solid,' he said sombrely, putting it to his lips and blowing hard – going red in the face with the strain. I could not help smiling – he looked a real picture, standing in a pile of pig muck, looking for all the world as if he was trying to play a tune on the vacuum cleaner. . . .

I became conscious of a sound behind me at about the same time as Stan. He stopped blowing, his mouth dropped open and terror filled his eyes. I looked round to see Alison turning into the drive, a shopping bag in each hand. She took in the scene in an instant, dropped the bags, and charged towards us like a maddened bull.

'What have you done?' she screamed.

'Oh . . . er . . .' I started to stammer, but before I could get my words out, Stan butted in.

'It's all right,' he said, trying to force a smile . . . and failing dismally. 'We just borrowed the van to take the school's pigs to the abattoir. Then the van caught fire . . . and we're just cleaning it up a bit.' I've got to hand it to him. He said it as though it was the most natural thing in the world. I was impressed.

Alison, however, was not. 'I don't believe it; you must be mad – both of you. Have you been drinking?' She spun round to face me, with anger in her voice. She went on, 'You must be mental – round the bend. Fancy trying to get pigs in the back of my van – my little "min"; and look at what you've done to the hoover!'

I was about to say something (though I do not know what) when she continued, 'Where's the carpet . . . and my flowers?'

'Ah . . .' said Stan, feeling a little more confident '. . . we left the carpet and the flowers at the school. Didn't want them to get damaged, you know. We'll pick them up tomorrow.'

'I don't want to hear any more from either of you,' she snapped.

'I'll go, then,' I said brightly. 'Er . . . sorry for the er . . . trouble.'

If looks could kill, I would have been dead on the spot.

'Just get in that house, Stan, and then I can have a real go at you – without half the neighbourhood listening.'

'Actually . . . it was my fault. . . .' I ventured.

'It was Stan's fault!' she replied, with a finality which precluded further debate on the matter. 'Get into that house, you big fool . . .' she said, pushing him towards the door.

I opened my mouth to ask if I could get a lift back to school . . . and thought better of it.

Stan picked up the carpet and the flowers the next morning. She was still not speaking to him, he said. I paid him for his time and petrol, and slipped him a couple of extra pounds. After school that day I popped into town and bought a large box of chocolates and a nice bouquet of flowers. I took them up to the house that evening. 'Min' was safely locked up in the garage. I sheepishly explained the whole story, but got a pretty frosty reception. They still were not speaking. The chocolates and flowers helped – but only time would heal the wounds.

When I got back home I took out my wallet and did some sums. I had spent as much on petrol, flowers, chocolates, etc., as I would have done to hire the livestock transporters in the first place! Never mind a profit – I was not going to break even ... so I increased the price of the meat by another penny a pound ... for 'incidentals', as it were!

I picked up the meat the following Wednesday. It was all nicely cut up into joints and chops, and packed into four large plastic bags. I put them on the back seat of the car, and smiled ruefully to myself as I drove back at the thought that the pigs were a heck of a lot less trouble this way.

They had the last laugh, though, for when I came to pick them up I saw that one of the bags had leaked – and the blood had stained the seat. It took me a good hour to clean it all off.

A month later I bought a tow-bar for the car, and a second-hand trailer. I somehow did not think Stan would be quite so obliging a second time.

More Calves and Some Visitors

PINKIE AND Blackie, the two calves, grew very well indeed. They became altogether too big for our potting shed, so it was time to sell them. They had been the very first livestock in our department, and so had become quite special. They had done much to help boost our image, giving us more credibility within the school and helping us along the path to our goal of becoming a registered smallholding.

They had been good for the pupils, too – certainly the fifth-year pupils who were responsible for them. We made a point of weighing all the food, since the pupils were carefully charting the cost of buying and rearing these animals. Each week, they were weighed and measured, and the results recorded and plotted on graphs. The pupils had fed them, looked after them, seen them disbudded, and watched them grow and develop. Now they were five months old, and so I contacted a local farmer, Mr Jack Pearce, to see if he might be interested in buying them. He came and looked them over, and offered us seventy pounds per calf. We calculated this would give us a clear profit of fifteen pounds per animal. Mr Pearce would keep them for a further thirteen months, and then they would be sold as beef. I softened the blow with the pupils by assuring them that we would straightaway buy two more calves – and they could always go and see Pinkie and Blackie at the local farm.

I involved the pupils in the whole deal, wanting them to understand the practicalities of running a farm. They calculated the cost of rearing an animal and balanced this against cash received. As the calves were loaded up into the cattle truck and driven off I basked in the knowledge of a job well done.

59

Not that my teaching experiences had always been so positive. I was reminded of a teaching situation which had not gone quite so well – a mistake I had made right at the start of my career.

I had only been teaching for about three weeks, and was giving a lesson on calf troubles and diseases. I was explaining that if you feed calves substitute milk from dirty buckets, or if the milk is given too hot, or if the calf is subject to draughts and chills or gets an infection, diarrhoea will probably result. This particular class had very little agricultural knowledge, and I found myself having to explain terms like 'in calf'. 'in lamb' and 'farrowing', one week.

'When a farmer buys a cow that is pregnant, he doesn't say "I've bought a pregnant cow." What does he say?' I asked in the lesson the following week.

Hands went up. 'She's in calf, Sir,' answered Nicholas Galloway.

'Correct,' I said, pleased that they had remembered that much, at least. You could never tell, with this lot. 'Let's see how many of these farming terms you can recall. If a farmer has a calf with diarrhoea, what does he say?'

This time, a puzzled silence settled on the group. 'I'll give you a clue. The word begins with an "s",' I added, helpfully.

'It's got the s. . . .!' yelled four of the coarser element, in unison. The class disintegrated into helpless laughter, and I was left somewhat embarrassed.

'No. Actually, the correct term is "scours", you'll remember,' I shouted, over the uproar, trying to regain control of the situation. If I dropped any more clangers like these, it would surely get back to the headmaster; we would be having yet another period of needlework on the timetable in place of rural studies . . . and I would be teaching it!

After the calves were sold, five of the boys worked hard cleaning out the shed, then scrubbed it all out with water and Jeyes Fluid. With the cheque it was our ambition to buy two more calves, almost immediately, along with some more laying hens, some timber, wire, nails ... and the thousand and one other things we had not been able to afford until that time.

But we were in for a shock. The county council appropriated all the income! They argued that since they had provided the money for the initial purchase, plus the money for feed, etc., then the 'profit' was duly theirs. In fact, much of the money for feed had come from the hours of hard work I had put in on Mick's cowshed. Perhaps I ought to invite the chairman of the county council to come and work alongside me next time. . . .

I was devastated. Every day for five months – Christmas Day and Boxing Day included – we had worked to rear those calves. Now the benefit of all that work was being taken away. Anger quickly replaced the initial sense of disbelief, and I made phone call after phone call to county council offices to try to get someone to see sense. It was the old, old story, being referred from one pen pusher to another, everyone trying to avoid making a decision by referring it to someone else. Finally, I got them to agree to let us keep the 'profit' part of the transaction – the thirty pounds – but they insisted that I sent them a cheque for the balance.

With those as the rules of the game, how could I ever build up the department? I felt totally frustrated. For once, the headmaster played the 'good guy'. He agreed to lend me two hundred pounds out of the school funds to get us going. Then we would establish our own farm funds. We would pay off the debt we owed the school in instalments, and all future income would be ours.

With the two hundred pounds I bought some more hens, some fencing posts and nails, timber, sand and cement . . . and two more calves. I got in touch with Lord Clifton, and he agreed to let me have two Hereford cross Friesian bull calves. Hereford cross Friesians are considered a better beef animal than a pure Friesian, though generally more expensive to buy. I went to look at the calves that evening. He told me that I could have two good strong red and white coloured calves for ten pounds a head cheaper than the black and white ones. That is because you cannot always guarantee that their dam was a Friesian. At market farmers would suspect that it might be a Hereford cross Ayrshire, or Hereford crossed with some other breed, and therefore not such a good beef animal.

I did not mind, and went for the red and white calves at the cheaper price. Money was tight. I knew that I would most probably not get as much when it came to sale time, but beggars cannot be choosers, and I needed to buy more foodstuff, too.

Lord Clifton delivered the calves the next day. They were an immediate hit with the pupils – and I had lots of volunteers again. It was now the end of January, and I had been teaching for five months. We had cleared all the weeds and dug over the ground. We had laid paving stones, planted some trees, shrubs and roses, dug out a duck pond and were keeping calves, pigs, poultry and rabbits. It was only a start, of course, but we were making progress.

Suddenly, out of the blue, a county council inspector dropped in on us. He seemed very impressed, and even offered to purchase a greenhouse. It was enough to make you believe in Father Christmas again, particularly after my past experiences with the council. The greenhouse measured ten by eight feet, and cost £144. We bought it in kit form, and spent many a happy hour trying to decode the instructions and figure out how it was to be erected. My fifth-year pupils were thrilled, since it took up many a lesson to get it finished.

One of the lads who helped me a lot was named Martin Towers. I had a phone call from his mother to say that he had had an argument with his father, stormed off, and had not returned home that evening. They were very worried. Martin had become extremely involved with the calves, and had never missed a single day in feeding and caring for them. It seemed so out of character that he would just vanish, and give no thought to the animals he loved. The headmaster came to see me, and we spoke to some of Martin's classmates. Nobody had seen him, though.

The police came into school and questioned me. They said that I was the only teacher he confided in, and they wanted to know if I could help them at all. Unfortunately, I could not. A photograph of Martin appeared in the local paper, with the headline: 'Have you seen this boy?' It was all getting very serious.

At last they found him – hiding out in some nearby fields. He had been hiding during the day and then, at night, creeping back into school and crawling through the window into the calf pen, where he had spent the night. He had done that for three days and nights before being discovered. I knew he liked those calves, but never suspected that he would move in with them!

Life went on, and over the next few years the department flourished and gradually expanded. Lawns were sown and vegetable, flower and fruit gardens were established. I was working all hours – skipping breaks and lunch hours, and spending time before and after school to get the jobs done. I even skipped an assembly or two – a 'hanging' offence, to hear the headmaster talk. The day-to-day

problems, though, were less a matter of straying boys . . . and more a matter of straying livestock. The hens were the worst. They were forever getting into other people's gardens – usually at assembly time – and I was constantly rounding them up and bringing them back. I wish some-one would cross a hen with a pigeon and come up with the first 'homing hen' – it would certainly make my life much easier!

One of my worst experiences of this kind began quite harmlessly at the end of an assembly. It had all been pretty much routine up until that point.

'I've got something very important to tell you,' said the headmaster, in his most sombre voice. 'Next Wednesday is a special day for this school. On that day we will have six school inspectors paying us a visit, and looking into every aspect of our work. They will be visiting certain depart-ments, talking to members of staff, discussing the syllabus, and looking at the amount and condition of the equipment we have here. If you see them, be polite and courteous – open doors for them or direct them if they look lost. Above all, be on your best behaviour.'

A special staff meeting was called on the Monday. We were told to put extra posters and charts on the walls, to have pupils' projects available, along with their exercise books. Staff were instructed to look smart, and to stand up to teach, not sit down. In short, the headmaster wanted us to pull out all the stops.

Our school has an excellent reputation in the area – second to none in the county in terms of examination results, for example. Parents from the other side of town would often specifically request that their children attended our school – so I, and the rest of the staff, thought we would have little to worry about. The headmaster was 'playing for keeps', however; determined to create the best possible impression.

The tuck shop was closed three days before the visit to ensure there would be no litter. The senior mistress even had her classes scouring the grounds looking for offending sweet papers and crisp bags. The children loved it; much better than lessons. The headmaster had bought a bottle of turpentine, and armed with this and a rag took to removing graffiti from the toilet walls. It was quite an education for him, I think.

The preparations went on apace. Colourful charts and posters festooned the walls; flower arrangements sprang up in the entrance hall; desks were rubbed down with sandpaper and scrubbed clean, and the school was spick and span from top to bottom.

In the rural studies department we had been at it, too. Our livestock are always kept in show condition, so that was no problem. We decided to spring clean all the pens, however – entering into the spirit of the thing. The calves were cleaned out and were given a fresh bed of straw. The chickens and ducks were attended to – and the duck pond was drained, scrubbed and filled with clean water. The rabbit hutches were cleaned and scrubbed – and everything gleamed and smelled of disinfectant. Not that it wanted doing, as such – but we wanted to play our part.

At last the work was complete; not a cobweb in sight, everything clean and tidy, and the pathways swept. We mowed the lawn, trimmed the edges, cut the hedges, pulled weeds, forked the rose beds and creosoted the fence. It looked so nice, I even took some photographs – for posterity, as it were – since I doubted that it would ever look like that again.

Overall, I was well pleased. I had just one reservation: the brick building where we housed the pigs. I had been pushing for an extension for quite a while. It had served its purpose, at the outset, but was now pitifully inadequate. I visualised an extension on the back, virtually doubling the available space. I made a note to ask the headmaster for some money from school funds, but thought it prudent to wait until the visit of the inspectors was passed and things returned to normal.

The great day dawned, and the inspectors arrived. The headmaster met them and took them for coffee – five middle-aged gentlemen, all smartly dressed and carrying the regulation brief-cases. Typical civil servant types. There was also a lady, equally smartly dressed, in a fetching pink outfit crowned with a large pink hat which must have been a good three feet across.

After coffee they looked around a number of the other departments and then came to mine. I met them at the door of my mobile classroom on the far side of the playground. I gave them a brief talk on the aims and objectives of the department, and they then wandered round the classroom, looking over pupils' shoulders, turning pages in exercise books, and asking questions. Then they looked through my carefully selected batch of pupils' projects – the ones that were legible and comprehensible. The lady in the pink hat was lapping it up. She was the sort with the piercing high-pitched voice and plum-in-the-mouth accent.

It was a lovely sunny day, so I thought I would take them outside for a walk around the smallholding. It quickly became apparent that they were all 'townies'. The nearest they had ever got to a farm was listening to 'The Archers'. I showed them the livestock, explaining in words of one syllable why we kept that animal, what we fed it on, and the benefits of giving the children this kind of hands-on experience. The livestock seemed to be co-operating much better than the children – though that was hardly surprising; the calves got up, stretched, and sauntered over. The visitors loved the rabbits – especially the little babies, which were just at the cuddly stage.

Then came the pigs. The lady in the pink hat said they smelt. Little did she know they had been cleaned out only the previous evening. I could not smell a thing. The pigs looked back disapprovingly, too.

A quick tour of the gardens followed – the lawns, flowers, vegetables and fruit were a little more up their street. Time went by quickly. Soon it would be time for lunch, and then on to the relative delights of art and needlework – much more up their street, I suspected.

They shook hands with me – albeit a little tentatively, I felt – congratulated me on my work, and said that they felt the department was a real asset to the school. The lady in the pink hat said 'Splendid, splendid!' I was warming to her, now – even liked the hat.

At four o'clock I went up to the staffroom. Mr Harris, the English master, asked me how it had all gone. 'Oh, excellent,' I said. 'They all seemed very pleased – especially that lady in the pink hat.' I just could not wait for the glowing words which would come my way from the headmaster once their report was submitted.

'Have they gone?' asked Harris.

'No,' I said. 'Miss Perrin, the home economics teacher is plying them with tea and cucumber sandwiches in her classroom. She has spent all day cutting off the crusts.'

'I think I'll go and join them,' said Harris, jokingly. 'I could do with a good feed.'

I walked back down to my classroom, still rehearsing how I would handle my conversation with the headmaster, and basking in its glow. My pupil helpers were finishing off the feeding. It was only just 4.15 pm, so I decided to do some marking. It is a bit like painting the Forth Bridge; something you never finish, as such. It is not my favourite job – but I was feeling good, so I got out a batch of third-year exercise books. One of the boys put his head around the door to say they had finished – all except David, who was still cleaning out the pigs. I nodded.

David was a nice lad; a bit rough and ready, but a willing worker. He had that magical ability – shared by a good number of boys – of looking permanently scruffy. I do not know how he did it. He would start the day clean, walk up the garden path, touch nothing – and immediately be dirty.

I sat down at my desk and began work on the pile of exercise books, with the successes of the day still at the forefront of my mind. A few minutes passed, and then, out of the blue, a pig shot past my window at about a hundred miles an hour . . . with something that looked remarkably like a scarecrow in hot pursuit. I leapt out of my seat. It was David, shouting and screaming and running hell for leather after one of the pigs – right across the playground. I dashed outside and shouted to him to come back. He turned, saw me, and ran back, yelling: 'The pigs, Sir . . . the pigs are out.'

'Don't panic!', I shouted. Then, fighting down the panic myself, I urged him to calm down and stop yelling. Glancing around I could count three of the four pigs, wandering happily around the playground. 'One missing,' I said. David nodded furiously and tried to splutter something – but he was out of breath. 'Don't explain now,' I said. 'Get up to the gate, look each way down the road, and beckon me if you can see it. If not, just stay by the gate in case these three try to make a break for it.'

David dashed up to the gate, looked both ways, and shook his head. At least we did not have that to worry about. We could concentrate on the 'three musketeers', and worry about seeking out the 'scarlet pimpernel' afterwards. I swung open the pig-pen door, and propped it back with a brick. Then I grabbed a bucket, filled it with pig meal, and scurried across to the pigs, calling all the time. Just for once they could not have cared less about food, revelling in their new-found freedom. I tried spilling some on the ground; no go. I was going to have to herd them – one by one, probably – or just plain grab them, and manhandle them back into the pen.

I was thinking a little more clearly now and realised the need for reinforcements. Could I rope in some others to give me a hand? I glanced at my watch. Blast! It was gone five. I looked round, frantically. Sometimes there were football practices or other extra activities going on. Nothing doing tonight, though. I caught sight of some movement in the first room at the corner of the school, next to the rear entrance. Great! Some pupils must have stayed behind to do some extra work. I started running across the playground – then slapped the anchors on when I suddenly realised that that was the home economics room, where the inspectors would just be sitting down to their tea. I did not think that the headmaster would relish a bit of pig-penning. I would have to manage on my own.

I did quite well, as it turned out, and the three pigs were soon safe and sound back in the pen. I was a bit out of breath, but unscathed. Now for the elusive Charlie – the biggest and boldest of the lot. He had vanished.

I ran up to David, who was still standing at the gates.

'Can't see it, Sir. Which pig is it?' asked David.

'It's Charlie. Would you believe it . . . but where on earth has he got to?' I decided to leave David by the gate, and work myself round the school, clockwise. I checked the tennis courts and round the back of the laboratories. No pig. I turned the corner and walked along the front of the school, then went right, into the staff car park. This was about the farthest point from the pig-pen, and I just could not see Charlie getting this far. Where had he got to?

I completed my circuit, and David came across to meet me. 'No luck, Sir?'

'No,' I said, getting more than a little worried by this stage. We walked back towards the pig-pens.

'He's there! He's there!' shouted David, pointing towards the rear entrance of the school. Sure enough, there was Charlie, nosing his way between the dustbins. I had missed him by not wanting to get too near to the home economics room.

Just as we saw Charlie – he saw us. Alerted by David's shouting, he bolted . . . straight for the open door at the rear of the school. David and I gave chase, but he had quite a start on us, and disappeared down the corridor. David showed me a clean pair of heels and was catching up with Charlie fast. Into the nearest classroom dashed the pig, with David in hot pursuit, just a yard or so behind.

'I'll get the bloody thing!' shouted David, now really into the thrill of the chase, as pig and boy disappeared through the door of the room. I rushed through the doorway, into the room . . . and froze. Before me sat the

headmaster and the school inspectors, rigid with shock, mouths open, cake in hand. Charlie shot under a stool – but was so fat that it got stuck on his back. He was careering round the room like a lunatic, with David stumbling and crashing after him. Nobody else moved – staring wide-eyed at pig and boy locked in the hunt.

Charlie was obviously scared out of his wits – squealing like mad – and did not much like the 'saddle' he seemed to have acquired. He did what all good pigs do at such moments of stress . . . stopped dead in his tracks . . . and made a mess on the floor.

'The pig's gone and . . . on the floor,' screamed David, pointing at the luckless pig. I wished the ground would open and swallow me as the headmaster's eyes met mine. I had repeatedly tried to drum into this witless boy that it was manure, muck or even faeces – but at this, of all times, he had reverted to that, of all words! The three lumps lay steaming on the floor, right next to the feet of the lady with the pink hat.

70

'I . . . I'll clean it up in just a minute,' I said politely. 'I'm just going to catch that pig first,' I added, as though it was the most natural thing in the world. By this time the lady inspector's face had gone as pink as her hat, and was reddening further with every second. I smiled weakly and joined David who, by now, had cornered Charlie. They were staring each other out in the far corner of the room, with Charlie continuing to squeal, somewhat indignantly, as though David had somehow broken the rules of the game. We made a grab for him, extricated him from the stool, and pushed him unceremoniously, wriggling and protesting, out of the door. The people in the room stared after us, in amazement.

'Charlie, Charlie, what are you trying to do to me?' I asked of the still-protesting pig. 'And as for you, David,' I snapped, 'What are you thinking of, using that sort of language in front of our visitors? You ought to be ashamed of yourself. I've a good mind . . .'

David retorted 'You'd have been in even more of a mess if I'd gone home.' I had to admit he was right . . . at least to myself. I said nothing, and we continued to push and shove old Charlie until he was safely back in the pen. Then we grabbed the cleaning bucket and returned to the classroom.

You did not have to be overly sensitive to detect the somewhat strained atmosphere which prevailed. We busied ourselves with cleaning up. David held the shovel, and I brushed the lumps of pig muck onto it. 'Take it and put it on the heap,' I said.

Shovel held level, so that the lumps would not drop off, he started for the door. Then, on impulse, he turned, walked straight up to the lady in the hat, and said: 'I'm sorry for the trouble I caused . . . and for swearing,' all in a very apologetic voice.

'All right boy,' she said. 'But do take that . . . that . . . that mess out from under my nose! I'm starting to feel a little sick.' Her colour, now changing to an interesting shade of green, gave credence to her words. David left.

I just did not know what to say or do, so busied myself again, this time in scrubbing the floor with a brush and some disinfectant. I glanced up and noticed a sausage roll and a half-eaten cucumber sandwich on her plate. I put the scrubbing brush in the bucket, picked up the rest of my gear, and made a dart for the door. Turning, I said: 'I apologise for our pig escaping and also for David's manners.'

'Thank you,' said the headmaster, through clenched teeth. 'That will be all, Mr Terry.' I reckoned it probably would. One of the gentlemen inspectors mumbled something about it being all right, and I backed out of the room, bowing slightly.

I returned to my classroom, but somehow did not feel much like marking exercise books. I stacked them neatly on my desk, locked the classroom and buildings . . . and checked the pigs again. Then I went home.

I did not get much sleep that night. Next morning I arrived at school extra early and fed the livestock, as usual. Members of my class drifted in, ready for me to mark the register. I started it without much enthusiasm. Mr Harris, the English master, came in. 'I'll take over, John,' he said. I looked at him quizzically. It was not like him. Harris was a real 'townie', and would never set foot on the small-holding, let alone do any work there. About the heaviest thing he had ever lifted was his pen.

'You don't understand,' continued Harris with a smirk. 'I'll mark the register. You have got to go and see the headmaster.'

I walked across the playground into the school, with about as much enthusiasm as a man walking to the gallows – and just about as slowly. Outside the head-master's door I ran a hand through my hair, straightened my tie, and brushed some of the surplus straw and hay off my jacket. My knock on the door was somewhat tentative, to say the least. 'Come in!' roared the voice from within.

I walked in. Looking me hard in the eyes, he walked up to me . . . past me . . . and slammed the door shut.

'What the hell went wrong with that pig?' he demanded. 'I thought you were supposed to be an expert in handling livestock? It was a disgrace – an absolute disgrace. And as for the . . . the exhibition the pig made of itself . . .' His face was now quite purple, and I was sure he was going to have a heart attack. 'What was David thinking about, using that sort of language in front of our distinguished visitors? Explain yourself, man!' He paused, and stared at me hard.

'I'll try to explain,' I mumbled – whilst at the same time wondering just what on earth I was going to say. My account of the afternoon's happenings was somewhat garbled, I suppose – but then the pertinent facts were already known . . . all too painfully so. I finished . . . and bit my tongue, as the headmaster let loose.

Funny, but all the time he was having a go at me, I just kept wondering whether I should raise the question of money for the extension to the pig building . . . or whether I should leave it till another time. I left it.

What Does Your Father Do?

RUNNING A SCHOOL farm was always going to be a challenge. Making ends meet was the name of the game, and my current need was for an extension to our existing brick pig building. It was no longer large enough – but I just did not have the ready cash.

Not that the school did not have the money. I happened to know that the headmaster had about five hundred pounds sitting in the school bank account, doing nothing. That would do me nicely.

However, after the inspectors' visit pigs were not the headmaster's favourite animals. In general relations were a little cool.

I was desperate for the cash. I had it all worked out in my mind. The extension would fit beautifully on the back of the existing building, which was sixteen feet long. It could come out some seventeen feet, giving me all the room I needed. But where would the cash come from? We had just had a jumble sale – for the Duke of Edinburgh Award Scheme – and the headmaster had organised a sponsored walk to buy a second-hand mini-bus just that month. Those two options were out.

Perhaps I could approach the local factory which made soft toys, and get my class to stuff them on a commission basis? I had a wonderful mental image of some of my 'toughs' sitting there, stuffing teddy bears! I nearly telephoned them straightaway, but this picture was replaced by that of the headmaster. I did not think he would accept 'child labour', however well-intentioned, when they were supposed to be having lessons. I could just hear him: 'What would the county council say? You're paid to teach, man, not set up a factory!' Back to the drawing board.

I now taught all age groups for rural studies but nobody was going to make a present of the money to me, so I wondered if there was some way my pupils could help. I decided to find out what jobs their fathers did. I started with a nice second-year class:

'What does your father do, Paul?'

'A barber, Sir.'

No good. I did not even bother to write that down.

'What about your father, Annette?'

'He's a builder, Sir.'

That's more like it. I made a note. 'And your father, Craig?'

'He's on the dole, Sir'.

'That's no good to me, Craig. The rest of you – I'm looking for builders, plasterers, carpenters and plumbers – that type of thing. Wait, though, if anyone is on the dole, they will have plenty of free time on their hands. I'll put them down for "labouring". What about the rest of you?'

A few hands went up. 'Julia. What does your father do?'

'He's the director of a firm that makes concrete building blocks.'

'You're joking! That's great! You could do very well in my class from now on.' The youngsters laughed, and the interrogations went on.

I spoke to about four hundred pupils in all. Most of the fathers worked in factories or offices, but there were some good avenues to explore. I had the concrete blocks man, a lecturer from the local technical college who taught woodwork, a director of a large firm of plasterers, a chap who worked for a double-glazing company, a manager of an outfit which fitted metal roofs, and an electrician. I still had not found an architect, a designer, a painter or someone connected with the readimix concrete trade – but I had not done badly.

I thought about writing one of my famous 'begging letters', but decided that the personal approach was a better bet. Dressed in my scruffiest garb (good for the sympathy angle) and using an old car I had borrowed from a friend, I hit the road. I felt a bit like a travelling salesman – something I had seriously thought about doing before opting for teaching. I had always had the 'gift of the gab', and had worked out my patter. I would get them talking about school and their children, then I would casually introduce the subject of the proposed extension. Only after they had volunteered some form of help would I raise the small point that we could not afford to pay anything!

It worked a treat. Of six calls, all offered help. Only the double-glazing salesman would not co-operate. He could see what was coming, probably too close to his normal patter. Not all the materials would be free – but the project was on.

My first job was to draw up my plans – front and end elevations and a list of the materials we would need. All the measurements and the details of drainage would also have to be covered. I did my best with my trusty twelve-inch ruler and the end product was reasonable – in my view, that is. The technical drawing teacher, Mr Parkes, thought otherwise, however, but took pity on me after he had poured scorn on my efforts.

'OK . . . when do you need the drawings by?'

'Oh, tomorrow will do,' I said.

'What! You've got to be kidding. It'll take at least till next week.'

The next morning he was there, though, with the plans. They were easily good enough to submit to the local council.

'You could get blood out of a stone,' he said.

'Thanks very much,' I replied, grinning sheepishly. 'Er . . . what do I owe you?'

'A dozen eggs,' he said resignedly. I had done business with him before and he was used to my bartering. I paid up.

Next day I took the plans in to the local council offices to apply for the necessary planning and building permissions. Sitting in the waiting room was rather like going to the doctors. It took as long, too. I must have sat there for an hour before it was my turn to go in. I was ushered into the inner sanctum.

'You need to submit the plans in triplicate,' was the clerk's opening gambit. One–nil to the council. Bureaucracies are fuelled by paper. They probably heat the council house with it – either that, or the hot air from the council chamber. It took me days to find someone with a photocopier that could cope with that size of document. Then it was back to the council house. Another hour-long wait, and then my turn.

'You need to submit the plans . . .' the clerk intoned.

'. . . in triplicate.' I finished, with a knowing smile. Two–one to me, since away goals count double.

Then it was all down to waiting. The council wrote to the neighbouring householders to see if they had any objections. After that, a formal notice appeared in the local paper. I was just glad it was not a twenty-storey block of flats I was planning to build. Finally, the much-needed permission was given – at least I think that is what the letter with all the 'hithertofores' and 'under sub-section 12' references was trying to say. These local council types never use one word where twenty will do.

We started digging the foundations the very day the permission arrived. We had staked it all out already, and I had been sorely tempted to have a little dig in the meantime. I had resisted. One of their spies might have caught me at it, and the headmaster would have seen to it that I was given a fair trial and shot, no doubt. 'What would the county council say, man. . . .' Those immortal words would haunt my every step.

True to form, as soon as we started digging, the monsoon broke. We spent as much time bailing out as actually shifting soil. Within a week we had dug the hole and the building inspector gave us the nod to carry on. We would put our rubble and hardcore into the hole. We soon ran out, however, and I was on the scrounge again.

'My grandma wants the brick wall in her front garden knocking down,' volunteered Paul. 'She says that if you do it, you can take all the bricks away.' I could have kissed his grandma.

I was even more delighted to learn that she lived just opposite the school. I had had visions of pushing barrow-loads of bricks five miles or so through the town.

I had plenty of volunteers for the work. My 'renegades' had certain talents in that respect, and it was a novel experience for them to use these legally. The old lady was most appreciative and, as we were leaving, her next-door neighbour came out and begged and pleaded for us to demolish her wall, too! Seemed to be catching on. I could see us turning professional. We ended up knocking down five walls in all – far more than we needed – but I was not grumbling, since the last wall we demolished brought us a small financial reward, as well as the – by now – superfluous bricks. We gratefully added this little windfall to our building fund.

The bricks and rubble soon filled up the base, and a layer of ash was added to fill in the gaps. We rolled the top and then put up the shuttering boards. We were ready for the concrete.

Unfortunately, I had not found a parent who was in that field, but I was still in contact with George Green, the supplier of our duck pond concrete. This time, though, we would pay. George agreed a good discount, and arrangements were made for delivery. Soon the concrete was in place, and we were ready for the blocks for the walls.

Julia's father, Mr Taylor, was coming to our aid with this. I had arranged to collect some free concrete blocks the following Monday afternoon. From another father we scrounged a lorry and driver for an hour or so. I took a couple of our strong lads to meet the driver and we made our way to the works.

At the back of the works was an enormous rubbish tip where they had dumped thousands and thousands of reject blocks. The tip was on the side of a quarry, with a two-hundred foot drop to the quarry floor. Now I am the sort of man who has no head for heights. I get dizzy one rung up on a step ladder. I was willing to give it a go, though. Greed, it appears, is stronger than fear, certainly as far as I am concerned.

We arrived to find Mr Taylor standing at the gates.

'Sorry,' he said, 'but I'm going to have to change my mind.' My heart sank. After all the hassle of arranging the transport, we were to be thwarted.

'Does this mean I've had a wasted journey?' asked the driver, looking at his watch.

'No . . . It's just that I don't think it would be safe to have you and the boys scrambling around on the tip – not with that drop, there. You see those blocks over there . . .' he said, pointing to a pile of concrete blocks neatly stacked on pallets, '. . . you can have those.'

They appeared to be brand new. 'They look splendid. Thank you very much,' I said.

'They are sound enough,' he replied, 'but if you look closely you will see that they are slightly different shades of grey.'

'I don't think the pigs will mind that,' I smiled back.

The blocks were loaded onto the lorry with a fork-lift truck, and within minutes we were on our way. When we got to school I gave the driver a dozen eggs – my standard rate – and thanked him for his help.

Our next 'volunteer' was Annette's father, Sid. He was a 'brickie', and had promised to lay all the concrete blocks free of charge during the evenings and at weekends. He made just one stipulation:

'I won't work on Fridays, though. That's my boozing night.' Far be it from me to come between a man and the finer things of life.

Sid was a real character. He was actually the boss of a small building firm in the area. He was enormous – looked like a wrestler – with a huge beer gut and bright red hair. I had bought in three tons of sand and ten bags of cement and borrowed a cement mixer. Sid agreed to start work that following Saturday, at 8.00 am.

I was up at the crack of dawn and met a couple of the lads down at school to begin the cement mixing. Eight o'clock came . . . then nine . . . and then ten. No Sid. I kept looking at my watch, and the boys kept adding water to the mortar. Eventually we had to admit defeat and throw away the rapidly hardening mixture.

Carol, Sid's wife, answered the phone when I rang.

'I'm very sorry,' she said, 'but he's in bed.'

Well, if a man is ill, that is all there is to it. I checked that he would be all right for the next weekend, and she confirmed that he would. I telephoned on the Thursday and was told that Sid would be with us at 8.00 am on Saturday morning, bright and early.

Saturday came . . . but Sid did not. Again, I had been silly enough to mix up the sand and cement. I telephoned Carol.

'He's ill, I'm afraid.'

'But I thought he was better?' I asked.

'He was . . . until last night, that is. He went out again, you see.'

'I don't see,' I replied.

'He got plastered again, and he's got the mother and father of all hangovers, this morning.'

The light dawned.

I rang again the next Thursday, and spoke to Sid this time. Yes, he would definitely be there on Saturday. True to his word, he was . . . at least in part.

'Haven't you got a silencer for that bloody cement mixer?' he whispered.

He looked like death warmed up. He was unshaven, with eyes like slits, and a complexion that had a definite tinge of yellow. He was stumbling around like a zombie, bumping into things with a pained expression on his face.

We had hoped to lay two rows of second-hand house bricks, then put a damp-proof layer in, then lay the concrete blocks on top. He laid half a dozen bricks, then had to sit down.

'I do feel bad,' he moaned. He sat with his head in his hands, murmuring '. . . never again . . . if I get over this. . . .'

Then he seemed to revive a little; became positively perky. He had been to a party, the night before – but had sunk ten pints even before he got there. The recovery was short-lived, however. His hands were shaking. He laid three more bricks, and then packed in for the day.

'I'm off to bed,' he said. 'Don't feel too good.' If looks were anything to go by, he was not far off the mark. I had seen healthier looking corpses.

'I . . . I'll come back tomorrow,' he mumbled.

He did not. Mind you, it was Easter Sunday. He turned up again the following Wednesday evening – and really got down to work on this occasion. He got through all the house bricks plus forty of the concrete blocks. He came back again the following Wednesday, but this time he had been drinking beforehand, and even brought some bottles with him. He spent more time swigging than bricklaying. Just my luck – to end up with a boozy bricklayer!

He let me down once more . . . and that was that. I telephoned him and told him that I thought it was better if we went our separate ways. He agreed. When he was sober he was fine – but the way things were shaping up, it would be the year 2,000 before we finished the job.

I went back to my line of questioning: 'Er . . . what does your father do . . .' was asked over two hundred times before I found a likely candidate for the treatment. I had to break out my tramp's outfit and borrow the car again, but it was worthwhile. Mr Garratt was most obliging, and very hard-working. He laid over a hundred blocks the very next Saturday morning, and finished the job the following week. He positioned the door frames, windows and the roof supports.

The lecturer from the technical college did a real craftsman's job on the window frames. He brought a group of his students over and they made some excellent doors. Everything was going just fine. All we lacked was a roof.

What Does Your Father Do?

Helen – a second year girl – had told me that her father was the manager of a firm which made metal roofing. I visited him, and explained that we had no money. Mr Stuart said that if I could wait they would probably be able to come up with some corrugated sheet off-cuts which would do the job. A month later they came.

The following Saturday Mr Stuart came to show me how to fit them. He put the first sheet on very quickly. I just watched.

'I'll do one more, just to make sure that you have got the idea,' he said.

'Yes, I reckon I could do it . . . but I don't suppose I could do it as well as a craftsman.'

With that, he set to, and finished the whole job.

I put up the guttering and the downpipes. Now I would just need the plasterers to come and render the inside and outside, and then the interior would be emulsioned.

I played my last card, and the boss of the plastering firm made arrangements for the job to be done. The boss had twenty men working for him, and a lot of work on their books. When they did arrive, it was in a very professional manner, however. The brand new lorry rolled in, loaded up with all the gear, three plasterers and a labourer. The lorry was followed by a sparkling new Rover; the boss was coming to supervise the job personally. Four hours later the job was done, and they vanished as quickly as they had come. The bill for their services? Nothing at all.

After the electrician had fitted some fluorescent lights, the council inspector came to approve the completion. It had taken seven months to build, but our £2,000-plus extension had cost just £450.64. Not bad, I thought.

I wrote to thank all those who had helped and sent them . . . you guessed it . . . a dozen eggs. Those eggs of ours were becoming the 'legal tender' for half the business deals in the town.

There was one final sting in the tail. The very day after

the pigs took up residence we had an unexpected visit from a county council official.

'Have you got planning permission for ... that?' he said with disdain, pointing to our lovely pig building. 'I must write to the headmaster about this. ...'

Castration

NOW WE had extended our pig-pen I could buy another four pigs knowing they would have plenty of room. Pigs are very useful educationally, and I was hoping the next four would make us a good profit. I would again buy them at about six weeks old, rear them until they were about eighteen weeks old, and then sell them as half-pigs for freezers. I was hoping to use the profits to buy some new buckets, feed troughs, gates, hurdles and a hundred-and-one other things which I desperately needed. There was always something – but we would never make enough profit to buy everything we wanted.

I telephoned my farmer friends, since I needed four pigs at the right price. Bert – one of our local farmers – said he was willing to 'do a deal'.

'I've got four good, strong weaner pigs that you can have cheaply – two gilts and two boars.'

I was interested. A gilt is a young female, which has not yet had a litter; a boar is a male which has not been castrated.

'We just haven't had time to castrate the boars. We're too busy at the moment, what with harvesting and so on. Still, you can do it,' said Bert.

'Er . . . sure,' I said, feeling a little unsure, since I had never undertaken that delightful task before. However, I did not want to blow my cover as a 'real' farmer so I said I was interested and Bert said he would get the pig movement licence which we would need.

Previously it had been the practice to castrate most male pigs which would eventually go for slaughter. People used to reckon that the meat from an 'entire' male pig had a strong taste – but I could never taste the difference. Still, older uncastrated males could be somewhat aggressive, and castration did solve the problem of unwanted pregnancies.

Now I had to find someone who could do the job for me. Bert rang to say that the pig licence had come through and I was to fetch the animals tomorrow.

I finished school at 3.45 pm the next day, quickly fed the livestock and put the trailer onto the car. David – one of my regular helpers – was to accompany me. He was used to pigs and had spent his lunch hour getting the pen ready.

'All done. Cleaned, disinfected, water in the bowl, straw on the floor – only the pictures to hang on the wall,' he joked.

I was certainly impressed with the pigs – four Welsh X Large White, six weeks old. They looked good and strong, with plenty of length to their bodies. The longer the pig, the more pork chops you get! I reckoned they would make ideal 'porkers', and were worth about twenty pounds each.

I'll take fifteen pounds a-piece for them,' said Bert. 'You're getting a bargain because I just don't have the time to castrate the two boars,' he added.

'I'll give you ten pounds,' said I, managing to keep a straight face.

'Come on, now!', said Bert, 'I'm doing you a favour at fifteen.'

After more bargaining we settled on fourteen pounds, and shook hands on it. To cap it all, I asked him for half a bag of his pig meal – and he agreed. Actually, it is good stockmanship to bring with you some of the meal the pigs are used to. That way you can wean them onto your mix gradually, and avoid the stomach upsets to which pigs are prone. Sensitive creatures, pigs.

We loaded the four snorting and squealing pigs into our trailer, and set off down the drive. I glanced back in the rear-view mirror to see Bert standing on the drive, cap in hand, scratching his head in a puzzled sort of way. Perhaps he was figuring how far he had been 'conned'! I put my foot on the accelerator and we sped farther down the drive. I did not want him changing his mind.

'You're brilliant, Sir!' said David. 'You really took him for a ride!'

I said nothing – but had to agree.

We got back and unloaded the pigs. They certainly did look good, but I knew it would now be best to leave them alone to adjust to their new surroundings. Animals are subject to a lot of stress when they are moved, so we closed the door to the pen and left them to it.

The following Thursday I was having a drink at the Black Horse, after our Young Farmers' meeting. I did the rounds of my friends and acquaintances to see if anyone was interested in a bit of castrating – as it were – but got no takers. The club leader suggested I try Mick, my old farm boss, whilst one or two others suggested I bring in the vet.

Calling the vet was not on. As usual, our school farm fund had only very little in it, so after school on Friday I got in the car and went to see Mick.

He was sitting in the house when I arrived. However, he did not want to admit that he had been taking it easy.

'I just popped inside to get . . . er . . . a screwdriver,' he said.

I outlined my little problem, and he agreed to come and do the job for me.

'I'll be with you next Monday. Don't let them run off in the meantime!' He grinned all over his face.

Beggars cannot be choosers, I am afraid. Mick was rough and ready; very coarse in his manner – but he was cheap. In fact he said he would do it for little or nothing. I could always buy him another screwdriver. . . .

That week I read up on castration in my pig-keeping books and my prized copy of *Black's Veterinary Dictionary*. Nothing to it, I reckoned. Mick said he would bring all the gear in his van, and I need not buy or borrow a thing. I was glad of that. In the textbooks, you needed a sterile scalpel, sterile blades, cotton wool, surgical spirit, mild antiseptic and something called sulphanilamide powder.

Seemingly, it was a two-man job: one to hold the pig and one to actually perform the surgery. The assistant would catch the pig and hold it upside down by its back legs. The whole of the scrotum is washed with warm water and mild antiseptic, then the area where the actual incision will be made is swabbed with surgical spirit. The testicle is held by the thumb and first finger, and an incision is made along its length with the sterile scalpel. The stone should then pop out of this cut, and the cords can be severed. The second testicle is dealt with in a similar fashion, and the incisions are dusted with the sulphanilamide powder to prevent infection. The pig is then returned to a clean pen with a generous supply of fresh bedding.

It all seemed straightforward. I went through it a dozen or more times, in my mind, since I did not want to look a complete fool in front of my pupils, and I could now tell them what to expect. I had seen the job done at college, but, thinking about it, had never actually seen Mick doing it on his own farm. Perhaps I had just been out on another job at the time.

Monday morning arrived. I briefed my class of 15–16-year-old boys and girls what to expect, and that a local farmer was coming to do the job.

'My grandad used to use two bricks to castrate his pigs,' shouted William.

'Did it hurt?' asked Jenny.

'Only when he got his thumbs in between!' was the reply.

'Townie' pupils just do not understand why castration of farm animals is practised, so I spent a long time talking about strong meat, aggressive animals and unwanted pregnancies. I was not sure just how it was going to go down, and could envisage pupils fainting or being sick. Perhaps they would take it out on the farmer?

'Couldn't we try it out on William, first?' asked Jenny.

'You haven't got a scalpel big enough!' boasted William.

I got them to write it all up in their books – how and why castration is performed, and then told them that anyone who wanted to watch could do so, but if they felt queasy, then they should just leave quietly. No one would make fun. All twenty-five wanted to watch – though I suspected this was just bravado, at least on the part of some of them. I just hoped they would not disgrace us in front of Mick, since he was doing us a favour.

Mick arrived ten minutes late, in his battered van. It was nineteen years old and I do not think it had been cleaned in all that time. The muck was probably all that was holding it together. In the front, on top of the dashboard and in the open glove compartment was a motley collection of petrol receipts, aerosol cans, old syringes, nuts and bolts and a hammer. The floor of the van was littered with straw, hay, sheep feed, cow muck and dog's hair. On the passenger seat sat Jess, his faithful collie dog. One window of the van was broken, and an old plastic fertiliser bag had been sellotaped over the hole.

'He's got calf-skin seats,' said Jenny, one of my more observant pupils.

I was just about to look, when she said '. . . only the calf is still in them!' I looked in the back to see a dead calf there, stiff with rigor mortis.

Mick jumped out of the van. 'Mornin',' he said. I just nodded.

'The pigs are in here,' I said, showing him the way. 'After you've finished we'll put the pigs in this clean pen.' I proudly showed him my clean, disinfected pen, with its bedding of nice clean wheat straw.

'Huh, we never bother to put them in a clean pen,' he said, disparagingly.

'Would you like to say a few words to the pupils, explaining what you're going to do?' I asked.

'Nope. You're the bloody teacher,' he replied. There were one or two sniggers from the pupils.

'Well, there's your bucket of warm water,' I said. 'Shall we give you a hand to get your equipment out of the van!'

'No need for that. I've got all the equipment I need here in my pocket,' he said, patting his thigh. 'Let's get stuck in!'

With a whoop, James – always an enthusiastic child – leapt into the pig pen, grabbed one of the pigs, and handed it to Mick.

'That's a gilt,' roared Mick. 'Fine teacher you are. I thought you would at least have taught them about the birds and the bees.'

James made a dive for another pig. This time he was lucky, and he passed the boar to me. I turned the pig upside down, holding him by his back legs, textbook style. He screamed and screamed. The neighbours must have thought someone was being murdered.

'There's your bucket of clean, warm water,' I reminded Mick. 'Have you brought some antiseptic!' I added quickly.

'Don't need no antiseptic,' he murmured, taking out of his pocket an old penknife and spilling a motley collection of sweet papers, odd bits of bale twine and heaven knows what else.

For a moment, it just did not register. Before I could blink he had folded out the blade and pulled down the pig's

testicle with his finger and thumb. In a flash it was all done, and the testicle was in his hand.

'Who wants this, then?' he asked, brandishing the testicle. There was no reply, but I noticed a slightly pained look on the face of one or two of the lads.

'These testicles are lovely in the frying pan with a nice bit of bacon. They give them a fancy name: sweetbreads!' There were still no takers. 'What about you girls, then? These things can do you girls more harm than a dose of anthrax,' he roared. Still no answer. I do not think many of them understood him . . . or even knew what anthrax was.

Still laughing, he threw the testicle in to the other pigs. They all pounced on it, pushing and shoving, and soon it was gone.

'They like it warm,' he said casually. Then he repeated the performance on the other testicle – quick as a flash.

'Er . . . what about the antiseptic . . . the sulphanilamide powder . . .?' My questions tailed off. He could do the job faster than I could ask the questions.

Soon the whole job was done.

'There you go. Now he weighs two stones lighter,' he said, popping the pig into the clean pen. Some of the boys laughed. 'I can't see the point of dirtying up another pen, just for castrated pigs,' he added.

By now James was well organised, and he handed the other squealing and protesting pig to me. I tipped him upside down, and Mick got to work. Out of the corner of my eye I noticed Roger – the biggest, toughest, roughest lad in the group – going an interesting shade of green.

'I've done well to stand this,' he mumbled . . . then fainted – out like a light.

He was a dead-weight to move, but we hoisted him over to the fence, and leaned him up against it. Mick just laughed.

'It's your fault,' I said.

'Fetch the lad a cup of tea and a fairy cake,' roared Mick.

I went on. 'I still think you'd have done better using sterile equipment and the antiseptic – you know, like it says in the books.'

'Books! The best thing you can do with those books is sling 'em on the compost heap!' He folded up his penknife – without even wiping it – and popped it back in his pocket. 'We've gone out of pigs,' he announced. 'I've got three bags of pig meal back at the farm. You can have them for half-price, if you want to come and collect them. They're in my way.'

Never one to miss a bargain, I said I'd be there at lunch time.

'How much do I owe you for the castration then?' I asked – thinking at the same time that his 'overheads' – antiseptic, sterile blades, etc., had been noticeable by their absence.

'Nothing,' he replied.

I was going to offer him a dozen eggs – our usual 'currency' – but I did not think the offer would hold much promise for a man who had fifty hens of his own. He climbed back into his van, and sped off.

Back in the classroom we had the final ten minutes of the

lesson to kill. I was at rather a loss for words. They had all made excellent notes on the whys and hows of pig castration. The 'why' was still the same – but the 'how' had suffered a little in the demonstration!

Jane piped up: 'How could he do that!'

'Yes, it made me quite sick,' chipped in Linda.

'Well, you were not as bad as Roger,' I said.

Roger had managed to walk over to the medical room for a lie down. I could have done with a lie down myself! I tried to explain to them that I could not agree with Mick's . . . er . . . approach, shall we say. I promised to go down to the vet and get some sulphanilamide powder to prevent any possible infection.

I headed straight off for the vet's to collect the powder. I had just enough time to go to Mick's place, and collect the pig meal. I raced up to the farm, and Mick gave me a hand to load the bags into the back of the car. Just then his wife called him in for his dinner.

'Come and have a drink of tea,' she said to me.

I followed Mick to the house. It was an enormous old building, but dirty inside. Apparently they had just one electrical socket in the whole place – and the television was plugged into that. At this time colour televisions were relatively few and far between – but Mick had one. It was gigantic. I have seen a smaller screen in some cinemas, and it must have been positively painful on the eyes in that lounge. A man must get his priorities right of course.

The living room in which the TV was situated was incredible. They had obviously decorated at some distant point in the past. They had not bothered to move the furniture and pictures, and had just papered round anything which got in the way. Newspapers were stacked high on the window ledges, yellowing with age. In the centre of the kitchen stood an old motorbike, still there from the days when I used to work at the farm. I never had been able to figure out what it was doing there. Mick and his wife just automatically walked around it. What a way to live!

However, his wife dished up a marvellous meal for him

and her – beef, Yorkshire pudding, roast potatoes, creamed potatoes, peas, carrots, and lashings of gravy. I sat there sipping at my tea and feeling quite envious, having skipped my lunch at school. I was starving. Mick polished off the huge plateful in next to no time, and gave an appreciative belch. It might have impressed an eskimo, but it did nothing for me.

'Where's my pudding, then, lass?'

'Be off with you! You're getting too fat – worse than them there pigs. It's time you went on a diet.'

He gazed, somewhat appreciatively, I thought, at his pot belly.

'But we always have pudding.' Now it was the hurt, little-boy tone.

'Not today,' she said firmly.

He got up from his chair and shuffled over to the window. I sat there, sipping at my piping hot tea, wondering what he would do next. He sorted through the fruit bowl, discarding bananas and oranges, and returned to his seat, clutching a large, rosy red apple.

'That woman's trying to starve me to death,' he complained.

She would have a job, I thought. He could have lived on his stored fat for at least two or three years. He reached into his pocket . . . and took out his penknife. Slowly, he opened it, and started to peel the apple. I just could not believe it – the very same knife he had used, not an hour or so ago, to castrate my pigs! He had finished peeling the apple and was now tucking into it, with gusto, as if he had not eaten for a week.

'Fancy another cup of tea, luv, and perhaps one of my cakes?' Betty asked me.

'No thanks,' I replied – altogether too quickly.

Funny, but I had just lost my appetite.

Kids and Kids

WE HAD SAVED our profits with the intention of buying a goat. I had looked at the eight recognised breeds of goat at agricultural shows and perused photographs in books. The British Alpine was the one that took my fancy.

It is a large, black goat with 'Swiss' markings – that is white facial stripes, white legs and a white patch on either side of the tail.

I had looked after the goats at college, but I had never kept a goat before. A goat, I felt, would be an ideal dairy animal – an easy animal for children to learn to milk on – and not likely to kick as hard as a cow! We could sell the milk, or even use it to make cheese or yoghurt. The milk could also be used to feed goat kids or orphan lambs.

Goat milk is very good for digestive problems and diseases of the skin, like eczema. It is also good for asthma or hay fever, and people who are allergic to beef protein are often advised to switch from cow's to goat's milk.

Friends who kept goats told me that all their goats gave a gallon of milk a day. This 'gallon a day' seemed to be a magic figure, referred to by all goat-keepers. Seemingly you are nobody in their eyes if your goat cannot match this mystical mark. Farming is full of these 'norms'. Talking in the Black Horse after our Young Farmers' meeting on Thursday evening, one chap is always going on about his 'lambing percentage of 200' or more, another man seems to milk nothing else but 'two-thousand gallon cows' – and, of course, everyone gets 'four tons of wheat per acre'.

I thought it would be a mistake to buy a 'scrub' goat from the local market, or one that was advertised in the local paper. She would probably not give much milk, or you would not be able to get her 'in kid'; she might well have horns and look absolutely awful.

I decided I was going to go about things the right way. I joined the county goat society – which sends out a newsletter every month and holds regular meetings for all those people interested in goats. It made a good class exercise, finding out more about these particular animals before buying one. Pupils did projects on the various breeds – housing, feeding, breeding, milking, and other aspects of general care. I wanted to warn them off the 'impulse' buying to which many people are prone, especially with pets. I wanted them to appreciate that it is a serious decision, and that it needs to be approached in a proper, methodical way.

I went along to a goat society meeting, taking with me a couple of my keenest pupils. It turned out to be very interesting, with a good speaker giving an illustrated lecture on kidding. After the meeting I sought out the madam chairman – a typical large 'horsy' woman, sporting a grey woollen suit and a tie. She knew everything there was to know about goats – I had to give her that.

I explained our situation – that we were running a school rural studies department and finance was not over-plentiful. I explained how useful a goat would be to give the children experience in milking and animal husbandry. She asked me what sort of animal I was looking for, and I explained that I wanted a pedigree goat and hoped eventually to keep perhaps two or three females, breeding them all to pedigree. We would have our own prefix, and register our young females. I really laid it on thick!

'You don't want much, do you,' she commented. 'Have you got a shed or other building to keep it in?'

I explained that we planned to build a suitable shed from some second-hand timber offered by a parent and some corrugated roofing sheets which I had been given. She told me to go ahead with the building and when we were ready she would help me to find a goat.

At the meeting I bought a couple of goat books, a collar

and lead, a goat chain and swivel, and took lots of leaflets dealing with every conceivable subject from poisonous plants to cheese-making. Still, they were free!

A few days later we fetched the second-hand timber on the school wheelbarrow. The first job, however, was to put down a floor. I was getting good at this. We dug out the hole, put rubble in the bottom, then a layer of sand, and then I laid some 3 ft by 2 ft paving slabs. I had bought the slabs cheaply from the council, but had no sand. I searched the neighbourhood for some builders and eventually I found some building a couple of detached houses. I traded some sand for our customary currency: one dozen new-laid eggs.

I sorted through the timber and decided to make the shed in four sections. Using 2 inch by 2 inch timber, I made a wooden frame, then nailed the tongue and groove boarding onto this. I left one side of the shed half-open, and put a second-hand window in one end. After making the four sections, the lads and I bolted it all together. We then put up some beams and installed the corrugated roof. The building was 10 feet by 8 feet, with a sloping roof. All we now needed was a door. They can be quite difficult to make and, in any case, I was now running short of serviceable timber. Where could I get one from, I wondered?

I did not need to wonder for long. Some workmen came into the school and modernised the boys' toilet. I just happened to notice that the old doors – painted bright blue – were thrown on the lorry, to go to the tip. After a bit of fast talking (and more eggs) I ended up with not one door, but ten! Never one to waste an opportunity, I asked the pupils to check whether any of their fathers wanted to buy a door; then we could use that money to buy our goat.

I selected the best door for the goat shed. It was complete with toilet roll holder, although I did not think the goats would mind that too much. I used two more of the doors to replace those on the calf shed, which were getting a bit past it.

I was then ready to ring madam chairman of the goat

society. She said she knew of a British Toggenburg milker and a British Saanen goatling for sale. No, I said, I had set my heart on a British Alpine.

'Mr and Mrs Austin, down at Stratford, may have a kid to sell. They have a really good-looking goat, which is worth a bit,' said madam chairman. This kid was a pedigree animal, from champion stock. The owners had indicated that they were going to sell it, and she advised that I should watch out for the advertisement.

'The only thing that worries me is that this particular goat may be a little out of your . . . er . . . price range,' she added. 'Mr Austin is very tight-fisted, so beware.'

I scanned the pages of the papers for a good three weeks before the advertisement appeared. It was early Friday morning and I wanted to strike while the iron was hot. I rushed to find the deputy head and explained the situation. He kindly agreed to find someone to cover my lessons for me and, grabbing a couple of my trusty helpers, I was ready to roll. The only problem was that I had no transport. Hurrying across the playground, Gary Walker asked:

'Where's the car, Sir?'

I explained that I had taken it in for a service.

'Oh,' he said, 'my father took his car for a service – but couldn't get it up the chapel steps!'

Right little joker, our Gary. I managed to bribe one of the members of staff to lend me his Cortina, although I omitted to mention that I might be bringing home a goat in it. I just hoped those hens would keep on laying, since I was rapidly running out of 'currency'. The car had no tow-bar, so I could not take the trailer. Just my luck to be without my car on this, of all days.

I knew that the man to whom the car belonged never drove it above 30 mph, so I gave it a treat and blew away a few cobwebs on the way down to Stratford. By ten minutes to ten we were there, making our way down the long farm drive. There was no one in the farmyard – except a couple of border collies and a Jack Russell terrier, that is. The terrier came snapping at my heels.

Kids and Kids

I knocked at the farm house door. Mrs Austin opened it, and invited us in. The house was enormous – a big, detached residence, obviously worth an awful lot of money. I explained that I had read the advertisement and would like to see the kid. She said that her husband was at market, and that he would really want to deal with any sale. I could see that she was not keen to take it any further, but she offered to let us see the kid which was six months old, called Anna – and perfect. She looked really smart, had nice markings, and was well developed for her age. She had a twin sister named Juliet who, I was told, was not for sale.

It was obvious that Mrs Austin knew very little about goats. She showed me Anna's mother, called Kim, who was an excellent milker. I saw her records, and she really did give a gallon a day, in the summer months! I reckon her kid would be worth around fifty pounds. Certainly, I was prepared to pay that.

'How much do you want for the kid?' I asked, trying to sound as casual as I could.

'My husband said forty pounds,' she replied.

'Oh that's just too high for me,' I said, shaking my head and beginning to walk away. I then went into my full, well-rehearsed 'poverty routine'. 'We're only a school, you know, not an established business. The children and I really wanted a goat . . . for educational purposes . . . but there we are . . . I suppose.' Mrs Austin was obviously taking it all in.

'I could give you twenty pounds, I suppose.'

'But . . . but that's only half the price,' she exclaimed. 'Yours is the first offer we have had; I may get lots of people replying to the advertisement. . . .'

'. . . But no one as deserving as us,' I quickly cut in. She was weakening. 'Look, I want to be fair, so let's settle on thirty pounds, then we're both doing well . . . you know, a quick cash-sale.' I gave her my most plaintive look.

'Oh . . . all right then,' she said. We shook hands, and the deal was sealed. I paid her the money, counting the notes into her hand. As I handed over the last pound, she said:

'Oh, I'm worried. What have I done? I'm not sure what

my husband will say. I really should have waited, you know. I don't think he's going to be pleased with just thirty pounds.' She was beginning to get rattled. 'Ah well, it's too late now. We've done the deal,' she said resignedly. I breathed a hearty sigh of relief ... and was all ready to make for the door.

We stood the goat in the back of the car, placing her front legs on the floor behind the front passenger seat and her back legs on the floor behind the driver's seat.

'Goats don't usually make a mess while you are actually travelling,' she said reassuringly, 'so just make sure you don't stop on the way home.'

I groaned, inwardly, at the thought of how many sets of traffic lights and road junctions we would have to negotiate.

'As soon as you get back to school, take her straight out of the car. I'll send the registration form on to you.'

With that, we set off. David sat in the back and held her in position. He was used to livestock – though pigs were his forte – and he was to keep the goat's rear end over a rubber

mat. I realised, though, that a rubber mat could only hold so much!

I was nervous, as we negotiated each potential hold-up – but Anna was excellent. We made it all the way, with no 'accidents'. I stopped the car and David immediately jumped out, taking Anna with him. I brushed out the car – and breathed a sigh of relief.

I put her in the newly constructed goat building but it took her some twenty-four hours to settle properly. She started to bleat as soon as we left her, but once she had settled down she rapidly became a firm favourite with the pupils.

Rumour has it that goats will eat anything. This is just not so. In fact, they are very fussy eaters. Anna – like most goats – would not eat any food that had been dropped onto the floor, and if as much as a piece of straw or hay landed in her water bucket, she would not go near it. True to her word, Mrs Austin sent on the registration form – but included a letter saying that they had subsequently received over forty enquiries for the goat kid – and that I was very lucky to get her for thirty pounds. She could say that again!

As she grew, Anna became quite a character. Her party-piece was hair pulling. Girls with really long blonde hair were prime targets. She would sneak up behind them, and pull it hard, with her teeth. She would then let go, open her mouth wide, show her teeth, and shake her head from side to side – a real goat laugh.

Female goats will only allow the male to serve them when they are in season. Although she came on heat a few times during her first autumn, like most goat breeders we did not put her to the male until the following autumn when she was eighteen months old. When goats come on heat they usually wag their tails a lot, and often bleat continuously.

I had made arrangements with the owner of a stud British Alpine male beforehand, so when I arrived at school, one morning, to find Anna bleating like mad, and wagging her tail, I was ready for action. Goat breeders tell me that the animals always seem to be on heat at the most inconvenient times. This was one such instance. I just could not get out of my lessons that day. I had also agreed to talk to the Women's Institute, at 7.30 pm that evening, but reckoned that I would just have time after school to have the goat served and then get to the WI.

I loaded Anna into the trailer, after finding two twelve-year-old volunteer helpers, Rachel and Rebecca. This was to be my first such experience with goats, and the goat farm was quite difficult to find. After getting lost a couple of times we eventually made it, and introduced ourselves to Mr and Mrs Keen. They were really nice people, and complimented us on how well our goat looked. Then the smell hit us. Male goats have a smell all of their own – once experienced, never forgotten! I can tell you this, they will never sell it as aftershave. In the mating season it is even more pungent.

The stud billy was a pedigree named Omar. The 'honeymoon' was to be a short and sweet affair. We introduced the happy couple in his 'bedroom' – a square building with whitewashed walls. He stood there, making a heck of a lot of noise. He was enormous, with a big black beard. Compared with our dainty-looking Anna, he was a real brute – very macho. He was somewhat lacking in the courtly graces, too. He offered her neither a drink nor a meal; what he had in mind was a little more basic. He sniffed her, all over. She just stood there, wagging her tail. Within two minutes he was down to business – and ten seconds later it was all over. I doubt if she realised what had hit her!

I had quite forgotten Rachel and Rebecca, my two helpers. They were standing behind me, rooted to the spot!

'I'm not at all sure you young ladies should be watching all this,' I said. 'What would your mothers, or the headmaster, say?'

They just giggled, and blushed. I must confess, the thought about the headmaster was a new one to me, too. Did his 'spy-network' reach this far out . . . ? I dismissed the thought from my mind.

I was given a service certificate and duly paid the stud fee. I half-wondered whether my 'eggs' were valid currency in this part of the world, but not even I could figure out what ten seconds of Omar's undivided attention were worth in terms of eggs! I paid up in cash.

We had a quick look at the rest of Mr Keen's goats, and then took Anna back for the 'second instalment'. Omar went for her immediately but, in his ardour, mounted her at the wrong end. Mr Keen shoved him off, and I held Anna as the billy lunged forward and served her for the second time. She threw her head right back and she arched her back after being served. These are two good signs, indicating that the mating has been successful.

We took Anna out of the 'bedroom'; the 'honeymoon' was over, and there was no time for farewells. We loaded Anna back into the trailer. Whatever else, Omar had certainly left his smell on her, and as Anna had rubbed up against me, my clothes were reeking of billy goat, too.

We thanked Mr Keen, said cheerio, and pulled out of the farm drive as a Land Rover and a trailer pulled in. Another 'client'; Omar was having a busy night. He must have thought it was his birthday!

I drove back as fast as I could and that is pretty fast. We reached the school at 7.00 pm, and I had to be at the WI for 7.30 pm. It would take me about twenty minutes to get there. We unloaded the goat, and I dropped the girls off on my way home where I had a quick wash and brush-up. Then it was off to the meeting.

I arrived ten minutes late. There they were, all sitting neatly in rows waiting for me to begin. I launched straight in, but after about ten minutes became aware of this horrible smell. Funny, where had I smelt that before? It was billy goat! I had forgotten to change, and the warm room was making it even worse. I gave them the shortened version of my standard presentation and sat down. The ladies on the front row were looking at me in a very strange way – and it was noticeable that no one came up to me afterwards to ask questions.

Anna did not come on heat again twenty-one days later or forty-two days later, which meant that she had not 'turned', and so was probably 'in kid'. The gestation period is about 152 days, and the pupils – especially Rachel and Rebecca – ticked the days off on the calendar, one by one.

True to form, the meticulous Anna gave birth on the 152nd day, producing two kids – one male, one female. The babies were well and strong, and the birth was particularly straightforward.

'The kids were dead on time,' said Rachel.

'No. Alive on time,' I replied. Rachel looked puzzled.

Most male kids are slaughtered at birth, because they are not very economical to rear. They drink gallons and gallons of milk, and even if you can find a customer to take them as kid meat, when they are about sixteen to twenty weeks old, they are not worth much money at all. You would actually be better off just selling the milk they consume.

Despite this, though, we decided to keep the male and rear him to about sixteen weeks. We have continued to do this. After the pupils have waited patiently for 152 days I have not the heart to kill the youngsters at birth – especially when twin males are born.

We also kept our first female goat, and called her Ruby, since the school was celebrating its fortieth anniversary. Ruby is now a grandma herself.

'Sir! Sir! Ruby's eaten the centre pages of my English book. It's my homework, Sir!'

I laughed at first. Gary Walker was a natural comedian, and I was sure he was teasing me. Just for once he was not joking. Sure enough, Ruby had scoffed the centre pages from his English book. It would have to be English!

'Well, you'll just have to go and explain to Mr Harris what has happened, won't you.'

'Oh, Sir! Mr Harris won't believe me, Sir! When I tell him that one of the kids ate my homework he'll think I'm having him on.'

I could see his point.

The next day, Harris cornered me in the staff room.

'In twenty-five years of teaching I've never come across such a thing.'

I played innocent. 'Er ... and what was that, Mr Harris?'

'That boy, Gary Walker, came to me with a preposterous story about one of your goats eating his homework book.'

I carried on nonchalantly sipping my tea. 'Yes, funny wasn't it. I didn't know they were interested in English.' He turned a strange purple colour, huffed and puffed, then turned and stormed out.

The next day I received a call from 'on high' – a summons from the headmaster. I knocked gingerly on his door, before being summoned to the 'presence'.

'You really must be more careful with your goat, man. You have certainly upset Mr Harris over this silly matter of the English book. Really, now, what would the governors say? Do you know, Mr Harris came to me and said that he was seriously thinking about giving up teaching. A man of his talent, too.'

'Sorry to hear that,' I said, lying through my teeth and trying desperately to fight back the smile.

The pupils often take the goats for a walk around the school grounds. They usually go through the staff car park and on into the playground, and visitors are amused to see three or four goats on leads, closely followed by the obligatory boy with the bucket, shovel and brush. That was another of the headmaster's edicts. Funny he did not want someone out in front with a red flag, too.

He came over to the rural studies department, and as it was not time for his annual visit I knew it was something important.

'Mr Terry – here a minute, man! I was driving my car, on the way to an important county meeting the other night, when there was this atrocious smell in the car. I looked down, and spotted goat . . . er . . . droppings all over my shoes! I must have walked through it on my way to the car park. It's just not good enough, man; not cricket, you know.'

I tried to explain, but could not get a word in edgeways. I resigned myself with thoughts of the 'they also serve who only stand and wait' maxim, through a discourse on his expensive hand-made shoes and the obligatory 'what would the chairman of the committee have to say' routine. Such is life.

Anna turned out to be a really good milker – although, I must confess, not in the mythical gallon-a-day class. After a month of being milked twice a day, she became very quiet and placid – ideal for the interested pupils to learn on. She was never known to kick; you could pull her 'inside out' and she would just stand there, without complaining. The best thirty pounds I ever spent, that animal.

One day, though, I was amazed to find one of my helpers – a boy named Timothy, who was supposed to be milking Anna – giving her the fresh, warm milk to drink.

'What on earth are you doing, boy?' I asked.

He looked up at me, smiled and said:

'Oh, it's all right, Sir. I got a bit of muck in the milk . . . so I'm just running it through again.'

Kids!

Building Up a Flock

I FELT the time had come to do something a little more demanding. The department was looking respectable and the area of wasteland had been transformed into a registered smallholding. This had been my ambition, but now this had been realised I needed a new goal.

As a boy I had bred and shown guinea pigs, rabbits and cage birds. I thought that showing some larger livestock could be the answer. I would have loved some Hereford cattle – but there was not room for them on our one-acre holding.

One of the fifth-year girls suggested that we grew geraniums for showing. She was very interested in them, but she would be leaving school in less than a year's time. I would then have to continue the project. Not that I have anything against geraniums, but I hardly thought I could become an enthusiast. Another pupil suggested we went in for growing enormous vegetables, such as bumper carrots, marrows or pumpkins. Interesting . . . but not for me.

No, it would have to be something agricultural, since that is where my main interest lay. Perhaps we could breed and show sheep. Now that was something which could really interest me.

So we bought two Kerry Hill ewes from a farmer in South Warwickshire. I had chosen the breed because they make marvellous mothers – they will go through fire and flood for their lambs, and give lots of milk to feed them. They are a good commercial proposition, too, with lambs that mature into first-class butchered meat; not as quick to grow as the Suffolks, perhaps, but much hardier. Their wool is fine and they are pretty-looking sheep, I always think, with that white face and black markings around the eyes and nose and with black and white ears and legs.

However, our original two ewes, Lucy and Cindy, had produced a disappointing crop of lambs. They had a great deal of black wool in the neck area, which is a fault. Kerry Hill wool is ideal for sweaters and jumpers, but the black wool is difficult to dye with white, cream or pastel shades.

Lucy and Cindy were the best two ewes we could afford at the time. Now, though, we recognised that we had to pull out all the stops and buy some top-quality stock. I wanted to build the flock into something in which we could really take pride.

I telephoned the secretary of the Kerry Hill Flock Book Society, and she gave me the names, addresses and telephone numbers of half a dozen breeders who would probably have what we were looking for.

I then telephoned all six possible breeders. Mr Stone seemed the most helpful, and I was encouraged to learn that his rams had been judged Champion Kerry Hill Sheep at the Royal Show in previous years. He lived at Knighton, Powys, and he suggested that I travel to Knighton, visit Knighton Show in the afternoon, and follow him back to his farm afterwards. Then, perhaps, he would be able to find us three suitable ewe lambs. Three pupils, all studying sheep for their CSE projects, would accompany me. They were Janet Webster, Stephen Blythe and Adam Rowe.

I met Mr Stone at the show. He was good enough to explain to me what was happening when the Kerry Hill sheep were being judged. I watched very closely, keen to learn all I could.

The rams are always shown singly; the ewes in pairs. The rams were led around in a circle, and the exhibitors then lined up in the centre of the ring. The judge started at one end of the line, looking very closely at each ram. The rams were then led around the ring once more, and the judge called them in, putting the best ram at the top of the line. The others were then sorted into descending order. The judge changed his mind from time to time, swopping one or two of the animals around – but finally his decision was made. Then the steward gave out the rosettes and prize cards.

Next it was the turn of the ewes. They were led into the ring, then stood in pairs. Again, the judge started at one end of the line, examining them closely. The pair judged the best were asked to go to the top of the line, and the rest of the ewes were graded in sequence.

I knew a bit about Kerry Hill sheep, but Knighton was the first time I had actually seen them being judged.

'The main thing the judge is looking for is black markings around the eyes and nose – very distinctive black markings, and not grey or brown,' explained Mr Stone. 'The ears should be set high on the top of the head, and the sheep should be as large as possible, with a strong, level back, wide loin, deep and well-sprung ribs, and with a good heart girth. The wool should be free from black markings. The sheep should, of course, walk correctly and the teeth should be perfect.'

My head was reeling. There seemed so much for me to remember – but I did learn a lot from that first show. I was very impressed with the winning pair of ewes, and got talking to their owner, a Mr Robert Porter. He was helpful, and gave me a couple of extra pointers about the breed.

I followed Mr Stone back to his farm, which was situated just outside Knighton. It was certainly a very picturesque area, with rolling grass hills – real Kerry Hill country. How nice it was to see Kerry Hills grazing in the lush fields. At home in Warwickshire I was used to seeing the Suffolks and Suffolk crosses which dominate the scene there, so the change was pleasing.

Mrs Stone greeted us, and told us that before we went to look at the sheep we were to 'have a bit of tea'. I was not going to object – and thought immediately of the 'cup of tea and a fairy cake' which Mick, my old boss, always used to talk about. I was wrong.

The table was laid – and groaning under the weight. We feasted on ham, beef, salad – with everything you could imagine – plus a sponge and a fruitcake (both home-made) and in addition the famous Welsh cakes. My pupils just could not believe it.

Afterwards Mr Stone took us out to look at his livestock. He told us that he had some 1,200 ewes on the farm – Kerry Hill, Clun Forest and Suffolk crosses. He had sorted out about thirty ewe lambs. The difficult job would be to choose just three.

Mr Stone was very good, and helped us pick out three which looked very similar. When you show a pair of ewes they should ideally look identical, and we bought three just in case one did not grow quite as quickly as the others. I paid Mr Stone, and we loaded the three lambs into the back of our trailer.

When they are registered with the Kerry Hill Sheep Society individual Kerry Hill ewes are given a number. Most farmers do not give them a name as well. I suppose when you have 1,200 sheep remembering names gets to be something of a problem. We decided we would give them names, though, and went for Sally, Sarah and Susie.

The newcomers settled in very well. I kept them separate from Lucy and Cindy. The new lambs were let out in the paddock during the day, and brought in during the evening. These three lambs were my very first show sheep, and I was determined to do everything right. Mr Stone had explained all about the feeding requirements, and I then had to put this into practice. We fed them, morning and evening, on what is called a coarse ration – mixing this with rolled oats

110

and a very small quantity of rolled barley, plus ad-lib hay, and a handful of cabbage, in the evenings. I had to start the ration off very gradually, since giving them too much could well have brought about stomach upsets. We started with a quarter of a pound, per head per day, over two feeds.

Mr Porter telephoned me: 'Mr Terry, you seemed very interested in the two ewes of mine – you know – the ones I was showing at Knighton.'

'Yes indeed. They are lovely,' I replied.

'Well, I've decided to sell them, by auction, at Welshpool. I plan to donate all the proceeds to charity – mostly for handicapped children.'

'I'd love to buy them.'

'The sale is next Monday.'

'Oh, no! That's the first day of the new term.' The realisation hit me hard.

'Oh dear,' said Mr Porter. 'Still, it's too good a chance for you to miss. I've shown this pair fifteen times, and they are unbeaten females – including champion females at the Royal Show.'

I was impressed. But I did not think this would cut too much ice with the headmaster – not on the first day of a new term, anyway! I thanked him for the information, and put the telephone down. What was I going to do? Mr Porter was right; it was too good a chance to miss. I would just love to have those two ewes. I could breed some super lambs from them – lambs with great show potential. I could see the ewes in my mind's eye; they were perfection.

Just my luck. If the sale had been one day earlier, I could easily have travelled to Welshpool. If it had been a couple of days later, I was sure I could have managed somehow. The very first day of term was a totally different proposition, though. I would have a new form – twenty-seven pupils, all newcomers to the school. I would have to play 'minder' to them, and, of course, they would have to go through the headmaster's famed 'indoctrination' monologue. I called it the 'ten commandments' – since it was all full of 'thou shalts' and 'thou shalt nots'. After that (for those who

111

survived) I would have to take them through the rules and procedures of the school – standards of work, school uniform, and a hundred and one other things. Then they would need to be taken on a conducted tour of the school to help them get the geography of the place. Life for the newcomers would be a bit difficult, and even more so with the form tutor not there. No, I stood more chance of winning the football pools than getting that day off . . . and I do not do the pools.

I tried to console myself. The price, I reasoned, would probably be far beyond my means anyway. These were champion ewes, and it was a special sort of sale where sentiment might play a part because the proceeds were going to charity. If I returned to school with an empty trailer it would just make it worse. Yet, I wanted those two ewes. I wanted them to breed from, especially. There are not many shows where you can exhibit older ewes. In a sense, it is a bit like a beauty queen becoming pregnant; her shape and figure will not stay the same. Once ewes have gone through pregnancy and raising lambs, neither their original shape nor their condition will have been retained.

I telephoned Mr Porter and explained the situation. He was very understanding, and suggested that if I wished he would find someone to bid on my behalf. If I was lucky enough to purchase them, he would take them back to his farm until I was able to collect them. I agreed, and asked him to explain to my proxy bidder that I was prepared to go up to £150 each for the two ewes. We agreed that I would ring him at his home at four o'clock to learn the outcome.

The day of the sale finally arrived. I sat through the headmaster's lecture with even less than usual enthusiasm. My mind was elsewhere. I took my twenty-seven new charges but – sad to say – my heart was just not in it. I kept thinking of the sale at Welshpool and those very special ewes, and the day dragged on.

At last four o'clock arrived. On the dot of four I rang Mr Porter. He sounded very cheerful and told me that it had been a tremendous sale, with a large crowd attending. All

the cups, rosettes and prize certificates had been placed on display and the auctioneer had described the awards the ewes had won. Television cameras recorded the whole thing, and there were many newspaper reporters. The drinks were free and he said I should have been there.

My thoughts exactly.

By this time, my heart had sunk. If it was as good as he was saying – and so well organised – then the ewes could easily have fetched a thousand pounds ... or even two or three thousand. I had visions of an entry in the *Guinness Book of Records*.

'Who bought the ewes, then?' I asked dejectedly.

'You did!'

I thought I must have misheard him, and asked him to repeat his answer.

'You bought the ewes. They belong to you, now.'

'But that's unbelievable,' I said, still too shocked for the realisation to sink in fully.

113

'Unbelievable it may be . . . but true, nevertheless. Yes, bidding started at £50 each, and climbed up and up. The final bid came in at £150. Your bid.'

'Great!' I replied, the truth slowly beginning to dawn.

'Yes, I'm obviously very pleased for you, though I had hoped they might have fetched a higher price – given that the proceeds are for charity. Do you think you could fetch them this evening? It looks a bit strange for the sold ewes to be still on my farm. I would not like anyone to think that it had all been a big fiddle.'

'Don't worry,' I said. 'I'll be along this evening, without fail.'

Only when I put the phone down did I realise what I had said. Our one and only trailer was in the local garage. Still, I could easily borrow another one from a friend in the local farming fraternity. Or so I thought. I broke the news to Adam, Janet and Stephen, and they were mad-keen to go with me to collect the ewes. I told them to check with their parents, then get back to school as soon as they could.

Three phone calls later, I was still no further forward. One trailer was out being used; one was off the road, like mine; one 'friend' just said no. By this time it was five o'clock – and I was in a predicament. Even if I found a trailer, I still had to drive the eighty-odd miles to Welshpool.

By now my three trusty helpers had returned to school – all kitted up with flasks and sandwiches, and ready to go. I could not possibly get the ewes plus the pupils in the back of my car, so I had to make a decision. The school mini-bus – a Ford Transit – was sitting in its garage, doing nothing. The headmaster had finished for the day and had presumably gone home, so I could not be expected to check with him for permission. After all, the PE teacher did not need permission to borrow the mini-bus for 'away' matches. He would just take it. That had to be the answer.

I still had that nagging feeling at the back of my mind, though. The last time I had borrowed the mini-bus I had really got into hot water. I had used the vehicle to pick up a load of manure. Unfortunately, one or two of the bags had leaked, and wet pig slurry had gone all over the floor. I had cleaned it out but Mr Martin, the maths teacher, had borrowed it that evening, to take the chess team to a local tournament. He and the pupils were all 'townies' and could not stand the smell, so they said. He had opened the window and put his foot down hard to try to get a bit of fresh air blowing through. He drove so fast that the cylinder head gasket blew. They were over an hour late . . . and, to cap it all, were badly beaten in the competition. Mr Martin had grumbled to the headmaster. I ended up on the carpet, of course.

The headmaster was keen on chess and its intellectual reputation, and blamed me for their unexpected defeat. When he got the bill from the garage he nearly had a heart attack at the thought of having to mortgage the school to pay it. I went into hiding for a day or two.

All these thoughts were in my mind as I walked over to the mini-bus. I called the pupils over and told them to jump in.

'We're not going for the sheep in the bus, are we, Sir?' asked Janet.

'Yes,' I replied, as calmly as I could.

'But won't they make a terrible mess, Sir?' queried Adam.

'Oh no,' I said, as confidently as I could – which was not very confidently at all.

We filled up with petrol, and set off. It was more or less a straight road to Welshpool, and I had made the trip there a number of times before. Finding the farm was a different kettle of fish, though, and that took about as long as the trip to Welshpool itself, or so it seemed.

Mr and Mrs Porter greeted us in the farmyard. Before we could look at the sheep, they ushered us into the house 'for a bit of tea'. We knew what that meant, after our experience with Mr and Mrs Stone – and did not object too much. Again, we had a superb meal – ham, cheese and salad, followed by trifle and cakes. After the meal, Mr Porter took us outside to look at the ewes. I was not disappointed. They were just as good as I remembered them, and I was itching to get them back home. We had taken a couple of hours over tea, and I wanted to get the pupils home, too.

'I've seen some unusual vehicles for livestock transit, in my time,' said Mr Porter, 'but this beats the lot!'

I explained that the trailer was off the road. We had to pick up the sheep to load them, and they trotted merrily to the front of the bus, as though intending to get a good seat by the window.

We set off. On the way home I just could not get the headmaster, and how he would react, out of my mind. I would have to tell him something. The school rules required that I fill out the record book for the journey, giving its purpose, the number of miles travelled and the quantity of petrol put into the tank. I half wondered about the feasibility of turning back the clock, but that was one skill I had not yet acquired. I bet some of my fifth-year pupils could have done it!

Time was getting on, and I was forced to drive back quite quickly. Suddenly, a small bat came from out of nowhere, and smashed into the windscreen. It was killed outright. It did no damage, fortunately. Being a true rural studies teacher I was able to explain that it was a pipistrelle bat, and that it was unusual for bats to do that sort of thing. They rely on echo location – a sort of radar – to find their way around. This one had obviously not had its mind on its work.

That set off a whole new train of thought. We got to talking about bats . . . then about vampire bats . . . then about vampires, and Dracula, and ended up telling each other ghost stories, in the gathering gloom. By the time we got back to school we were all thoroughly scared out of our wits!

We arrived back at ten minutes to midnight and un-loaded the two ewes. We put them in with Lucy and Cindy. You could certainly appreciate the quality of the two new ewes compared with the others.

I took home three very tired but contented pupils, then went back to school. It was well turned midnight before I finished scrubbing out the mini-bus. I kept sniffing, but knew that my nostrils were unreliable. My sense of smell had long since gone in such matters, and I just had to hope that all would be well. I dutifully filled out the record book, put the van away, and called it a day.

I made a point of getting into school extra early the next day. The ewes seemed to have settled down well. Now for the tricky bit.

I made a point of seeking out the headmaster during the morning break. I thought I would use a bit of psychology, and hit him with the good news first.

'Oh . . . er . . . we were lucky enough to buy those two champion Kerry Hill ewes yesterday,' I said, enthusiastically.

He looked up from his coffee. 'Excellent, Mr Terry. I am pleased.'

He did seem it too, I had to admit. I pressed on. 'Er . . . there is just one thing . . .' He paused in mid-sip. 'As you know, the trailer is off the road, so I . . . er . . . had to collect them in the school mini-bus, during the evening.'

The slight wavering in my voice betrayed the way I was feeling.

'What!'

I thought he was going to explode.

'Er . . . in the mini-bus, Headmaster.'

He went quite pale. 'It's not being used for a chess match today, is it?'

I assured him that it was not, and he breathed a huge sigh of relief. I had got away with it.

We named the two ewes Jemma and Jenny. They were doing fine, as were the three lambs I had bought from Mr Stone. We sheared the lambs on Christmas Eve. We shear them at this time of year so that their wool will be at its very best during the show season. If show sheep are sheared during May or June, then they will have altogether too much wool on them for the early shows, but not enough wool for the shows during the rest of the year.

The morning of their shearing was to be their last fling out of doors for some little time. With their fleeces gone, we would need to keep them indoors. Gradually, we would increase their ration, until after Christmas they would be eating nearly three pounds of concentrates per head per day.

All the time I was looking after these show sheep, the other four ewes – Lucy, Cindy, Jenny and Jemma – were put to a ram sold to us by Mr Stone and no doubt were enjoying their 'honeymoon'. I paid yet another visit to Mr Stone and could not resist buying some more ewes which had been with the ram and were hoped to be 'in lamb'.

Time flew by, and by March the three show ewes were eating three and a half pounds of concentrates each per day. On top of that they were eating cabbage and, of course, as much hay as they liked. They were eating me out of house and home and they would not produce lambs until the following year.

Our flock was increasing, and I was looking forward to our first show season, due to begin in the middle of May. I had a feeling that it would really put our flock on the map.

Lambing Time

LAMBING STARTED during March as expected and our Kerry Hill flock had expanded quite considerably. The lambs born to Jemma and Jenny were superb – certainly a cut above the rest. All our sheep were of course pedigree and were registered with the Kerry Hill Flock Book Society.

Over the years we built a good, general-purpose farm building, extending it in bays when we could afford to do so. Part of this large building is used to in-winter our ewes. From about January 1st and through the rest of the winter we keep them indoors all the time. The idea is not – as some imagine – to keep them warm, but to keep them off the pasture.

Our pasture is very well stocked in the summer and autumn, and it does it the world of good to rest it over the winter. The combination of winter rains and the hooves of the sheep will play havoc with the pasture, so that in no time it looks like a well-used football pitch. The grass is worn away, and the soil structure is impaired. Wet conditions also encourage footrot, a bacterial disease of sheep which can make them lame – so, all in all, in-wintering has much to commend it.

There is an additional benefit. It makes life a heck of a lot easier and more comfortable for the poor old stockman . . . me!

During the last week in December the ewes come inside for the nights only. They are fed good-quality hay, but no concentrates. After a week of acclimatisation, they then stay in all the time. They continue to receive hay, 'ad-lib', and then we start to give them concentrate feed eight weeks before lambing. A ewe is actually 'in lamb' for 147 days, but it is not until the last eight weeks that the foetus really begins to grow. We feed a 'coarse ration' which is a mixture of palatable sheep foods, including locust beans, linseed cake, protein pellets and flaked maize. We start with a quarter pound, per head, per day, in two feeds, and build this up slowly. At a month before lambing, this will have increased to one pound, per head, and at lambing time, will have gone up to two pounds.

The ewes are all kept together in the building with a stocking density of about sixteen square feet per ewe. At least a fortnight before lambing is due to begin we will have made some individual 'mothering-up' pens out of some hurdles. We put the mother and the new-born lambs in these pens, so that they can get to know each other without interruptions. Sheep are inquisitive animals and some of the ewes which have not lambed would tend to get in the way. Some would push the new-born lambs around a bit with their noses; others would become very maternal. One of our ewes is a natural mother; she takes it into her head to adopt any lamb which she sees, 'talking' to them, and even licking them dry. The pupils call her 'auntie' or 'nanny'.

The new arrivals stay with their mothers in individual pens for a few days. If all is well they are then moved into a general group at the other end of the building. In good weather they go outside in the daytime and return to the pens just for the night. Nothing looks nicer than a field containing newly born Kerry Hill lambs. The pupils and visitors just love it, and it does the school a lot of good.

About two weeks before lambing, the ewes are injected with a clostridial vaccine, which will protect the lambs – via the mother's colostrum – against eight diseases, including lamb dysentery and tetanus. The injection gives the lamb protection for the critical first twelve weeks of its life.

As the actual lambing time draws near, I try to get organised by collecting together all the various items I shall need. We keep some colostrum in our freezer, in case we have a ewe which lambs and produces no colostrum.

Colostrum gives the lamb protection against diseases, and contains vitamins and protein. It also has laxative properties.

I use a lubricant when I need to put my hand inside a ewe. This may be necessary when we have a difficult lambing, or when we are faced with a malpresentation. I use good old-fashioned Lux flakes for this, since they are very kind and gentle.

I place iodine on the new-born lamb's navel. This protects against joint-ill, a disease which affects the joints. The bacterium gets into the bloodstream via the navel cord.

I also keep a few bottles and teats, just in case a ewe produces little or no milk. Sometimes, too, the lamb is born too weak to suck from its mother, and then we use a stomach tube to feed colostrum into its stomach.

We have syringes and needles of all shapes and sizes – and keep a supply of magnesium solution, calcium borogluconate and, of course, antibiotics. The magnesium solution is for a magnesium deficiency called hypomagnesaemia; calcium borogluconate is for calcium deficiency, or lambing sickness. Until now we have been fortunate enough not to be troubled by these. Antibiotics, like penicillin, are used on many occasions. If I put my hand inside a ewe to examine her or to assist with lambing, then I inject her with antibiotics afterwards to guard against infection.

The lambing season plays havoc with my time schedules. I check the ewes after each lesson, at break, lunch times and after school. It is necessary, too, to check during the night. I live a mile away from school so, unlike most farmers, who live on site, just the sheer task of getting to and from the farm is time-consuming. If I rush, I can get up, get dressed, drive to school and make the checks, and then return home and get back into bed in about thirty-five minutes. I will generally go back to school at some point during the evening, just before going to bed, and then once or twice during the night. What I see, on each visit, determines when the next visit needs to be made.

If a ewe is close to lambing I will stay with her, of course. Sometimes, I have to wait for hours; other times, it is over very quickly. Once or twice I have actually spent the whole night there. Believe me, it is difficult to lose a night's sleep, be involved in lambing, and then come up smelling of roses and looking and acting like superman! When I have spent the whole night with the ewes, lambing, the last thing in the world I need is to mark registers, teach lessons and . . . especially . . . attend assembly. I cannot quite get the headmaster to see that, though. I try to dash off home, have a quick wash and change my clothes, and then I feel a little more able to cope with the rigours of the day.

A daytime lambing makes an interesting lesson for those of the class who want to be involved. One or two pupils will always be extra keen, and will actually help by holding the ewe for me if I have to lamb her.

In fact, most of our Kerry Hill ewes will lamb unassisted. The breed, generally, are very good at getting down to the job, although some will need help. The lambing percentage of 175 is readily achieved, however.

With a practised eye, it is usually easy to spot which ewe is going to lamb next. When lambing is imminent, her udder will fill with colostrum; she will be uneasy and will start to scrape the ground with her foot. She will keep lying down, then standing up again, and then will start to strain. A water-bag appears and then, hopefully, two fore legs and the head of the lamb. If the fore legs and the head do not come first, this is what is known as a 'mal-presentation' – and this will need correcting. There are different types of malpresentation including: two lambs trying to be born simultaneously; a lamb being born head first, with one or both of its front legs back; and the breach presentation.

Mind you, the business does have its funny side. I had returned to school one evening, at about seven o'clock. I was on my own, at first, but was soon joined by Ian, the caretaker's son, aged four.

'Can I help you, Mr Terry?' he asked.

'Yes, if you're a good lad, and don't make any noise,' I said with a smile. I did not expect any ewes to be lambing, as it happened. I had left them only an hour before, and all was quiet. I knew his mother was not keen on him watching a lambing, but I did not want to hurt his feelings. He could help by giving the ewes a few cabbage leaves. Our sheep like greenstuffs, and he would enjoy feeding them.

When I walked into the sheep pen, though, I found a ewe in some difficulty. I immediately slipped off my jacket and pullover, rolled up my sleeves, and got down to work. The ewe was straining and when I looked I could see that the head of the lamb was out; but no legs. They were both back. Using my Lux flakes for lubrication, I pushed the lamb back into the womb, when the ewe was not straining. Out of the corner of my eye I suddenly became aware of Ian. He was sitting on a bale, sucking on a piece of straw and watching me intently.

I was worried about letting him stay there but just did

not have the time to take him back home – things were too far advanced. I continued pushing the lamb back into the womb, and managed to locate the front legs. I straightened them, carefully, and brought the fore legs and head into the normal presentation position. The lamb was born, and I was feeling pleased with myself. Upon closer inspection I realised that my relief had been premature; the lamb looked to be dead. I grabbed it by the back legs, shook it roughly, and smacked it. Success! It spluttered . . . and started to breathe.

A voice came from behind me 'It serves the little beggar right for crawling up there in the first place!'

Soon the lamb was up on his legs. It was a big ram lamb, and weighed some fourteen pounds. The ewe did not have another lamb, but I was not surprised. This one was quite big enough. The ewe started licking him immediately. It was her first lamb but she was going to be a good mother. I always like to see the lamb have a good feed of colostrum, before I leave. This ewe was full and the lamb was eager to drink.

Not all our lambing stories end as happily as this one but on the whole we get relatively few problems. I was glad that Ian had witnessed a 'happy ending'. His mother took it well, too. She told me that he talked of nothing else for days.

A breeding flock of ewes is very good, educationally. The pupils can learn much more from practical experience with livestock than they would ever learn from simply referring to 'page 49 of the textbook'. Many of the younger pupils enjoy working with the lambs, and many older pupils choose sheep for their examination project. They can study many sheep topics, including the year in the life of a sheep, selecting the breeding ewes, culling out the old ewes, flushing, mating, feeding, lambing, worming, shearing, dipping, selling lambs and showing.

A few pupils choose to concentrate on lambs for their project. This involves recording the date each ewe is due to lamb, then recording the actual date of birth, logging the birth weight of the lambs, and going on to weigh each lamb, weekly. Graphs are then made of growth rate records to illustrate weight gain. Ram lambs not needed for breeding purposes are castrated by means of a rubber ring on the scrotum, above the testicles. The ring cuts off the blood supply, and in time the testicles drop off. We no longer castrate, as an entire lamb tends to grow more quickly.

Some years ago I was particularly proud of one boy's project. His written work was very neat and tidy, and his lambing records were excellent. He drew some fine graphs and arrived at some very sound conclusions. Reviewing it with him before the examiner came in to mark the projects, I suggested that he could improve it by illustrating it with some photographs and perhaps some visual aids such as wool samples. I saw the lad, three weeks later, and reminded him that the examiner was paying us a visit very soon.

'Have you illustrated your project, Mark, as I suggested?' I asked.

'Yes Sir. I've taken some photos and got one or two interesting visual aids,' he replied.

'Good lad. I hope the examiner will give you full marks – twenty out of twenty. You deserve it. You've really worked hard.'

'Thank you, Sir,' he replied.

The next Tuesday morning, the external examiner arrived and began working through the pile of projects. They were usually very good, and this year was no exception. He picked up Mark's project.

'This looks excellent.'

I agreed. He started to go through it in detail. The written work was superb, and it was all well laid out and nicely put together. I was pleased to see that Mark had indeed taken my advice, and that there were some very good photographs included, too. The examiner was clearly impressed, and nodded approval.

He turned over one page, though . . . and was stopped in his tracks. There, stuck on the page with sellotape, was a pair of withered lamb's testicles, complete with rubber ring still attached at the top. They were labelled, very neatly: 'Thomas's Testicles'.

'Well, that's certainly put me off my dinner,' chuckled Mr Venables, the examiner. 'Was this your idea, Mr Terry?'

'Well, yes and no. I did encourage him to put some photos and visual aids into the project . . . but was thinking more in terms of wool samples.'

He looked through the project, but could find no wool. He gave the project nineteen out of twenty marks.

I was disappointed. I felt that it was worth full marks, and said so to Mark when I saw him later that afternoon.

'You spoiled it, I'm afraid, by sticking those testicles in there. The examiner did not exactly approve. He gave you nineteen out of twenty.'

'Sorry, Sir. I did try to get some wool samples. But, don't you remember – you had just sheared the sheep!'

Richard, Oh Richard!

EVEN BEING charitable, I think I would have to describe Richard as a 'slow learner'. He was the sort of boy who could never quite get his thoughts and his words in line – much to the delight of his classmates. Not that he did not try – nobody could accuse him of that. Many pupils, when asked a question, would just say, 'I don't know', or be equally noncommittal; not Richard. He would always have a go. I had to admire him for trying!

Richard was really out of his depth on his first day at school. It is tough for any new boy – but for Richard it was the equivalent of being in a foreign land, with no friends . . . and not knowing one word of the language.

Richard, Oh Richard!

The new intake had all been shepherded into one of the large main halls and were seated, awaiting their introduction to the school. The headmaster arose, resplendent in his gown, to begin his 'Ten Commandments' speech.

Most of the pupils had never seen or heard anything like this before, and sat there wide-eyed and wide-mouthed. The headmaster was waxing lyrical by now.

Suddenly, the door at the back of the hall started to open and, since the windows were all open, the draught caught the door and it slammed open so hard that the glass nearly fell out! Every eye in the house was now turned on the pitiful-looking figure framed in the doorway. Richard.

'Why are you late?' boomed the headmaster.

You could have heard a pin drop. Two hundred and thirty-nine heads were now turned to the back of the hall. Before the boy could answer, the headmaster roared out again:

'Turn round! Who told you that you could all move your heads!'

In a splendid display of synchronised head-turning, two hundred and thirty-nine heads turned back to face the front.

'You haven't answered my question,' snarled the headmaster.

'I . . . I'm sorry I'm late, Sir . . . but I overslept,' answered a timid little voice.

'Save your pocket money then, boy, and buy yourself a decent alarm clock,' came the retort.

'Yes, Sir.'

'What's your name, boy?'

'Richard Keightley, Sir.'

'I'll be watching you from now on,' continued the headmaster, in his most sinister voice. 'Straighten your tie, and sit down.'

With that delightful tugging movement which comes as second nature to all boys he wrenched at his tie, so that it now resided somewhat left of centre, rather than off to the right, as before. His blazer was obviously a hand-me-down, and he looked as though he had slept in his trousers. His shoes were all scuffed, and his hair had not been combed for weeks.

The headmaster resumed, and after his speech the names of the pupils were called out by the year tutor, grouping some twenty-six or twenty-seven into a form. The form tutors then escorted their newly assigned charges to the new form room and went through the minutiae of lunch rotas, homework procedure, standards of work, school uniform, etc. To the new pupils the school was a veritable maze, so they were given a plan of the school and, to be doubly sure they did not get lost, the form tutor took them round the school to familiarise them with the 'geography'.

Mr Petty was the form tutor for class 2S3 – Richard Keightley's form. After the introductory talk all twenty-seven members of 2S3 set off for the grand tour. Mr Petty pointed out the cloakrooms, toilets, the library and the science laboratory. Not surprisingly (since Mr Petty was the woodwork teacher) the delights of the woodwork room came in for more than their fare share of attention. Rural studies, however, was given a miss. 'Not worth going down to the digging department,' claimed Petty. The tour over, the group then trailed back to the form room ... all twenty-six of them. Richard had vanished.

Fifteen minutes later he still had not turned up. Mr Petty asked a senior pupil to go and find him and, ten minutes later, the boy arrived, with Richard in tow.

'Where on earth have you been?' asked Mr Petty.

Richard just looked at his shoes, and made no reply.

'I found him in the toilet, Sir,' chipped in the senior pupil. One or two of the class sniggered.

'Come on lad, explain,' said Mr Petty.

'I didn't have time to go before I left for school, Sir, 'cos I overslept ... and I was having a bit of trouble, you know.'

'Out of 240 pupils, how come I landed up with you!' roared Mr Petty.

Richard had no answer, and went back to a bit of shoe inspection. 'S ... sorry, Sir,' he stuttered.

'Sit down, lad. I don't want to hear another word from you!'

Richard shuffled off to his seat, and Mr Petty got back to business, handing out the personal information form which each pupil is asked to complete for the school records. The form is confidential, of course, and asks for the pupil's name, address, telephone number, parents' occupations, etc. The pupils were given fifteen minutes to fill out the form, and soon the classroom was quiet as they got to work. When they were completed the forms were taken to Mr Petty. He briefly checked them over. One form posed a problem, however. It had no name on it at all.

'Who filled in this form?' asked Mr Petty, waving it in the air. There was no answer. 'Come on, it must be one of you.'

'I think it must be mine,' piped up a little voice from the back. 'Yes,' said Richard, 'I think it is mine.'

'Put your name on it then, you stupid boy!' roared Mr Petty.

Richard took it back, wrote his name on the top, and returned it to Mr Petty. The form was put away, with the rest, in the desk drawer.

The next day Mr Petty began sorting through the forms, in earnest. They were always a mixed bunch. Some were filled out meticulously and neatly; others were a bit scruffy, with doubtful spelling, and so on. One form stood out, however. The handwriting looked as though a maimed spider had dragged itself out of an inkwell and lurched across the paper in a somewhat haphazard fashion! If it got one out of ten for presentation, then, for content, it had to be in the minus range. Under 'Father's Occupation' the luckless boy had written 'shit metal worker'. That form made it onto the staff notice board, under the heading of 'quip of the week'.

I must confess I like 'characters'. In a perverse sort of way, I was looking forward to meeting this lad. I would have to wait until Friday, though, since that was the first lesson I was to teach to 2S3.

However, on Wednesday morning there was a timid little knock on my door. I opened it to find a 'new boy' there – a boy with a strikingly round face, a short back and sides haircut, and a blazer and trousers some three sizes too big.

'Mr Petty has sent you this note,' he explained, handing me a folded piece of paper. There were just three words on it, written large . . . with two exclamation marks. It said, succinctly, 'This is Richard!!'

I thanked the lad, and had a smile to myself. He had obviously not peeped at the note. Interesting, that.

On Friday he was as good as gold. I outlined what rural studies was all about – the syllabus, the nature of the department, and so on. I then took the pupils round the farm and gardens, pointing out the salient features. I kept half an eye out for Richard, but he was fine – fine, in fact, throughout the next three lessons, too. He had obviously settled down. Perhaps it was just nervousness on his first day, and perhaps Mr Petty had exaggerated. He seemed no trouble to me.

It was not until the sixth week that he opened up in class. We were doing a lesson on birds, using some colour slides I had taken and talking about a few of the common species. I talked about the resident birds of Britain such as the song thrush, robin and blue tit, and we discussed how we could help these birds by judicious winter feeding. I was pleased to see that a number of pupils already had bird tables at home, and that they used them regularly.

During the second part of the lesson we turned our attention to the subject of migration. We talked about the birds which are summer visitors to this country – birds like the swallow which arrives in April from the warmer climate of North-West Africa. I explained that the swallow will spend the summer here, feeding on insects taken on the wing and normally rearing two broods. During October, as the weather becomes colder and the food supply becomes scarcer, they take to the wing once more, and return to Africa.

We discussed, too, the winter visitors we have – birds which migrate here during the winter from colder climates. I gave the example of the fieldfare, a species of thrush, which arrives in Britain between late September and the middle of December and then returns during April to Norway, Switzerland, Siberia or Greenland to breed.

Exactly one week later we had our next lesson.

'We studied the topic of birds, last week. What can you remember? Fiona, can you tell me what we mean by a resident bird?'

'Yes, Sir, that's a bird that doesn't leave this country; it spends both summer and winter with us,' answered Fiona.

'Correct. Well done, Fiona. Now Richard, tell us what is meant by "migration".'

There was a long silence, while Richard gazed into space, seeking inspiration. The process looked positively painful. He screwed up his face, grimaced and looked in agony, such was his concentration.

'Well ... I'm not exactly sure, Sir ... but I think "migration" is when my mother gets those bad headaches.'

We all burst into laughter while Richard, open-mouthed, just looked puzzled. He went as red as a beetroot. At first I thought he was joking, but I could see, pretty quickly, that he had been serious. It took me a few minutes to restore order, and then assure him that his mother's headaches were probably attributable to migraine, not migration.

At the end of the lesson I watched the pupils trail back across the playground towards the main building. Richard was still coming in for some 'clog' from one or two of the others who were holding their heads and shouting about their terrible attack of 'migration'. I felt quite sorry for him, and wished I had not laughed.

About a month later, the topic was cereal crops. Wheat is used for flour and biscuit-making; oats, for animal feed and human consumption, I informed them. Eighty per cent of the barley crop in this country is used for livestock feeding, with the remainder going for malting. Malting is when barley is completely soaked in water, and then germinates. It is allowed to grow for a week, and the growth is then stopped by a heating and drying process. The resulting grain is then called malt, and is used to make spirits, beer and vinegar.

I explained all this, using one or two witticisms to help keep their interest.

'Since we are talking about cereals, we will have part one this week, part two of the "cereal" next week, and part three, the week after!' The class groaned. 'Well,' I continued, 'I couldn't think of "oat" else to say ... and "wheat" a minute, there's "barley" enough time to finish this lesson.' By now the class were squirming. 'I don't know "rye" I bother telling you lot these "corny" jokes! I'm simply "amaized" you don't all laugh.' The lesson ended in a crescendo of boos, hisses and cat-calls.

The following week I reviewed the lesson with them.

'We were talking about cereal crops, last week. Let's see how much you can remember. Robert, can you tell me what wheat is used for?'

'Er . . . it's made into bread, flour and biscuits – that sort of stuff,' he replied.

'Well done! Yes, that's right. Lucy: What cereal crop do we feed our sheep on?'

'Oats, Sir!' she said brightly.

'Correct. Now, Richard, what is "malting"?' As soon as I asked the question, I realised I had made a mistake. I had just picked him at random, but immediately wished I had not. Still, he could not do it again . . . could he?

He went into one of his ceiling-pondering routines, grimacing with concentration. Finding no answer on the ceiling he scrutinised the floor, but found no solution there either. Then a smile broke out on his face – he positively beamed.

'I'm not exactly sure, Sir . . .' (my heart sank) '. . . but I think that "malting" is what my cat does when it loses its hair,' he replied. Again, everyone burst into laughter, though this time I managed to keep a straight face.

'No, I think you mean "moulting", with regard to your cat, don't you, Richard?' He nodded. 'What I'm referring to is "malting" – what we do with barley. Tell me about that.' To my surprise, he did . . . and remarkably well, too. One or two of the class looked disappointed, and I noticed that he was still coming in for some ridicule as they left at the end of the lesson.

His first examination paper did not take long to mark; his answer page was mostly empty. He had had a shot at answering one question, though: 'What do we call the group of trees which produce cones?' Most of the class had given the correct answer, 'conifers'. Richard had put 'carnivores'. I got this sudden mental picture of trees going on the rampage, eating people.

Part two of the examination consisted of essay questions. One essay title was: 'Explain how milk gets from the cow to the doorstep'. I had some good essays on that.

Richard's, however, was a classic. The last sentence simply read: 'Milk is delivered to the doorstep by dairies such as the Coop and Urinate.'

That he reached the third year at all was something of a minor miracle to me. I had to admit, though, that he had improved with keeping. He was always a willing lad – a trier – and so I offered him the chance to come with me to a sheep sale at Knighton in Powys. He leapt at the chance and his parents wrote thanking me for offering to take him.

As we travelled up the A5, towards Shrewsbury, he was very excited. Chances like this did not come his way all that often, I gathered. The road, at one point, passes under a bridge built by Thomas Telford. The Birmingham-to-Liverpool canal runs over the top of it. As we went under we could see some boats passing over the top and Richard became very animated.

'Look, Sir! It's an oviduct!'

I smiled. 'No, I think you mean an aqueduct.'

I have to hand it to him, though, he was well-behaved, interested and I am sure he learned a lot. I was really pleased.

By the fourth year he had improved even more, only occasionally reverting to his former self. I remember one lesson I taught on the subject of poultry. This is always one of my favourites, since we can have a bit of fun. After going through the fact that a gander is a male goose, that a male duck is called a drake and that a pullet is a young female hen I asked the class what you get if you cross a cockerel – a male fowl – with a waitress. They looked puzzled but intrigued.

'It's easy,' I said. 'What you get is a chicken that lays tables!'

I even told them the story about when I was nine years old my mother sent me to the butchers to buy a chicken for Sunday lunch. The butcher asked: 'Do you want a pullet?'

'No . . .', I said '. . . just wrap it up and I'll put it in my bike bag!'

I asked the class some questions on what we had learned. 'Pam, can you tell me what we call a male goose?'

'Yes, Sir. A gander.'

'Robert, what is a male duck called?'

'A drake, Sir.'

'Correct. Richard, what is a pullet?'

'Well, Sir, I'm not exactly sure ... but I think it's something you put strawberries in when you're out doing some picking.'

There were those on the teaching staff who despaired of Richard. Mr Petty even nicknamed him 'Pilgrim', because he 'made very little progress'! By the fifth year, though, he was a different lad altogether. He had started to work very hard, always completed his homework on time, asked sensible questions ... and had learned to say 'I don't know', like the others, rather than have one of his 'I'm not exactly sure' shots at it.

He surprised us all, though, by getting a CSE grade 1 in his rural studies examination. Who would have thought that he would really make good?

A classic case of making a silk purse out of a sow's ear, you might say!

137

Showing

THE THREE ewe lambs we had bought from Mr Stone, in August, looked well. Susie, however, had outgrown Sally and Sarah, as sometimes happens. Since ewes are shown in pairs, and the two should look identical, it meant that our show pair would be Sally and Sarah.

A few weeks before the show season was due to begin I sent off for the entry forms. I had decided to enter four shows and filled out each entry form, sending them back with the cheques for the entry fees.

The ewes had been sheared on Christmas Eve and kept indoors after that. We had taken them out only for periods of training to walk with the halters. Halter training on the playground also gave them exercise. We kept them very clean right throughout the winter, but their wool was in need of a shampoo. Show sheep are only shampooed once – six weeks before the first show. I had never shampooed a sheep before, and did not quite know what to expect.

Janet, Stephen and Adam came into school especially early, one Saturday morning. I had everything organised and we decided to practise on Susie first, since she was only our reserve show sheep, just in case anything went wrong. I had all the equipment – buckets, shampoo and a hosepipe.

We cleaned out and washed down the building, because it was obviously no use putting clean sheep back into a dirty pen. We hosed her down, from top to bottom, then mixed up the sheep shampoo in warm water. We brought Susie over, and tipped the warm shampoo solution onto her back, rubbing it in with our hands. She just stood there, wide-eyed, not quite knowing what was going on. We tipped her up, and did the 'underside' – her chin, stomach and between the back legs. Everything was going really well . . . until we put her back on her legs, only to find that her backside, which had been on the concrete, was now dirty again!

Having experimented on Susie, we were much more organised with Sally and Sarah. This time we tipped them up and did the underside first. Then, and only then, did we do the top bits. I must say, they did look nice. Their fleeces had come up really white, with all dirt and grease removed.

'They look lovely, Sir,' said Stephen.

'Yes. I'm very pleased with our morning's work,' I replied.

'It's taken three hours, though,' said Janet.

I had lost all track of time in our involvement with the task, but could well believe it. I could not check, since I was – as usual – without a working watch.

'I am absolutely wet through!' said Adam. As the biggest and strongest of the bunch, he had had the job of holding the sheep down, while the rest of us did the washing. As such, he had received more than his fair share of both the shampooing and the rinsing.

We were all so engrossed in poor old Adam's plight that we took our eyes off the sheep for a moment. Fatal. Sarah, our best ewe, pulled away from Janet, and ran off.

'You dozy girl!' shouted Adam. 'Now look what you've done.'

'Don't panic,' I said reassuringly. 'She won't go far. Not with these other two here.' The other two, up until then, had been standing as good as gold on their halters. As if to cue, though, they both looked at me . . . and promptly bolted after Sarah, with the pupils in hot pursuit.

Sarah loved it. She was free after all this time indoors, and sped quickly across the lawn, past the rockery, and straight for the goldfish pond. I had been meaning to clean out the pond for weeks. It was pretty dirty – so dirty and clogged up, in fact, that all the weed on the surface made it look just like solid ground. Sarah obviously thought so, too. In she went, at full speed, making one heck of a splash. She sank like a stone, and when her head broke the surface again she was coughing and spluttering like a drowning man.

I glanced round. My three helpers had now managed to corner the other two sheep, and were in the process of putting them away. I ran to the pond, and helped keep her afloat. The four of us then tugged and pulled her onto the paving stones at the edge. I have never seen anything like it. She had gone in white and beautiful; she came out looking like a beached whale – all black and slimy. In her wool we could see all manner of little insects, tadpoles and water snails. Her head was covered in green slime, Canadian pond weed and bits of water lily.

'Why on earth did you let her go?' I shouted at Janet, losing my temper at the sight which confronted us.

'I'm sorry,' said Janet, almost in tears.

The two boys did not help. Following my cue, they pitched in to her, too.

'All that work, Janet, and now she will have to be washed again,' said Adam.

At that point a goldfish popped out from under a weed on her back and fell onto the path, wriggling and squirming. Stephen made a dive for it, picked it up, and threw it back in the pond. The pond itself looked as if a bomb had hit it.

Sarah's wool had acted like a great big sponge, and in taking her out we had almost emptied the pond. In the bottom was a layer of thick, black sludge.

'I hope the goldfish will be all right,' said Janet.

'Don't worry,' I said, a little calmer now. 'It could have been a lot worse. At least the sheep isn't injured.'

Sarah started coughing and spluttering again, and I half expected her to cough up a goldfish or a frog. I tell you – much as I like sheep – it would have been a 'short straw' job, if one of us had had to give her the kiss of life.

We picked the weed off her, and then started all over again, shampooing and rinsing. When we had finished, I personally led her back to her pen. I was not going to risk another accident.

A week later it was time to clip them. We carded them, first. A carder is a tool made up of small wire hooks which is run through the wool to lift it and help get all the knots out. It is a bit like combing – but with a wire brush. The sheep do not mind it, though. After carding, we trimmed them with some hand shears, making the back level and the sides straight, clipping hard under the chin and around the side of the face.

We then card and trim the sheep every week throughout the show season and on the day before, or morning of, each show. Their fleeces are only washed the once, however.

Our first show was the Shropshire and West Midland, at Shrewsbury. This is a two-day show, with Kerry Hill breed classes. The smaller shows do not have a separate Kerry Hill class. All the breeds are judged together with, say, a class for rams, a class for lambs, and one for ewes. I prefer the specialist classes, so we were to make our debut at Shrewsbury.

I loaded the two ewes, putting in with them a bale of hay, a bale of straw, a water bucket and a bowl of food. I remembered, too, to take our stockman's passes and our exhibitor's number. Checking that we had not left anything vital, the three pupils and I climbed aboard, and we were off.

I took the sheep to the show on the Tuesday evening, to get them settled in. The show itself is on the Wednesday and Thursday, and the sheep would not come back home until late Thursday afternoon. Mr Porter's was the first friendly face I saw. I proudly took down the back of the trailer, sure that he would be pleased with what he would see. I was wrong. He looked them up and down with a practised eye, and told me that the carding and clipping was just not good enough. I slipped a halter on each ewe and asked him to show me what he meant.

'Well, I'll help . . . but I can't clip them too well, or they might beat my sheep!' he said.

'I'll leave it to you,' I replied, somewhat crestfallen.

He worked away for a good two hours. When he had finished I could understand what he had meant. He had done a fine job, and they certainly looked better. The problem was that I had just not appreciated how high the standards were. I felt quite confient again, though . . . at least until he let down the back of his lorry and showed me his sheep. They were immaculate. Much better than ours, I was sure.

'Have you got your bags?' asked Mr Porter, casually.

'What bags?' I did not know what he meant.

He gestured over to the pens. The other Kerry Hill exhibitors had tied clean hessian sacks on the inside of the hurdles which made up each pen. The bags, tied against what might be dirty or rusty hurdles, would help ensure that the sheep stayed clean.

'I didn't realise that I needed to bring bags,' I confessed.

Mr Porter smiled, and assured me that I could borrow some of his. I had so much to learn.

We tied the bags on the inside of the hurdles, bedded the pens with clean straw and placed our two ewes inside. I was sure they stood a better chance now that Mr Porter had carded and trimmed them.

Most exhibitors sleep in their stock wagons or trailers for the duration of the show. I had decided to travel home with the pupils and meet them again the next morning. We all met at 5 am. The pupils were very keen, and that showed in their promptness. By seven o'clock we were at the show ground. The first job was to give the sheep a light feed. I did not want to give them too much since, like humans, that would have tended to make them sleepy. I wanted them to be wide awake.

I gave the ewes another card and trim to freshen up their wool. Judging was at ten o'clock, and we had to wait for the aged rams to be judged first, followed by the shearling rams and ram lambs. Then it was our turn.

Janet and I led our two ewes into the ring and stood them close together. Mr Porter followed us in, as it happened, and his ewes stood next to ours. Again, my heart sank. His were certainly the better pair. The judge worked his way down the line, looking at each pair in turn. He would take a general look, both front and back, and would then move in for a closer and more detailed inspection. He felt their backs to see if they were in good condition. Well-fleshed animals will do better than bony specimens. He checked the wool for black − especially in the neck area. He checked the markings on the face and legs, making sure they were black and not brown or grey. He was looking for sheep which had erect ears and good teeth, too.

Down the line he came, like a sergeant-major making a parade inspection. It did not take him long to sort out the best pair, and Mr Porter's ewes were sent to the head of the line, followed by the pair which Mr Williamson had entered. We were placed fifth. I was disappointed, I suppose. Still, it was our first show . . . and we had not come last. I had set my heart on a place in the first three, though. I think the pupils were disappointed, too, and we did not say much on the way home. There was still a lot we had to learn.

It was back to the old routine the next day. I was teaching for the greater part of the day, but returned to the show after school to pick up our two ewes. Showing was certainly going to mean driving a high mileage. I had driven 420 miles already.

The next show was in June. That was the Three
Counties, at Malvern. I was not surprised at the result – not
when I saw Mr Porter, Mr Stone, Mr Williamson and a
number of other by now familiar faces. Mr Porter won . . .
and we were fifth, once more. The Royal Show, at
Stoneleigh, near Kenilworth, Warwickshire, was the next
one on the calendar. This was very much 'home ground' for
us . . . but still the result was the same: fifth.

Next we had a small, local show. There were no specialist
classes, here, so I would not have competition from either
Mr Porter, Mr Stone or Mr Williamson. There were classes
for a ram, ram lambs, and three ewes. Finally, there was a
class for three butcher's lambs. For this show, Sally and
Sarah were joined by Susie, our reserve ewe, and were
entered in the three ewes of any breed class.

We were the first to arrive in the sheep section. I dutifully
put hessian sacks on our pen, and then unloaded the three
sheep. They did look nice. Other exhibitors arrived. There
was quite an assortment of breeds: Suffolks, Dorset Horns,
Leicester and Jacobs. We had not raised our hopes too high,
since I had been told that the Suffolks usually won. They
are a bigger, meatier sheep than a Kerry Hill. They are the
breed of sheep most often kept in this area, and hence the
ones with which the local judges have most familiarity. In
this case, it appears, 'familiarity' with the 'breeds' does not
bring 'contempt'!

We took our three sheep into the ring and stood them side
by side. The judging seemed to take ages – but, to our
surprise, the judge told us to take them to the top of the line.
This was our first taste of this somewhat heady experience,
and we would make the most of it. I expected at any
minute, though, that we would be ousted by three Suffolks.
It was agony. My heart was pounding. Janet, Adam and I
kept glancing at each other nervously while watching out
for any tell-tale sign of another trio of sheep coming to take
our place. We did not speak; afraid to break the spell.

The judge returned for a second look at our sheep. Then
he signalled the steward over . . . and he presented us with

the winning red rosette and prize. The presentation was made to Adam, who enthusiastically shook hands with the judge and the steward.

'Congratulations,' said the steward.

'Thank you very much,' we said in unison. He could see that we were all very pleased, and just smiled.

The steward then passed on to the second trio – Suffolks, as it happened – and presented them with the blue rosette and prize card. Another trio of Suffolks were placed third, and received the yellow rosette and prize card.

We led our sheep back into the pen, feeling elated. Our very first win! All was not over, however. The first prize ram and the winning ram lamb were brought out, to find the Champion Male; the older ram won it – a Suffolk. Then our three ewes were pitted against the three butcher's lambs, to find the Champion Pen of Sheep. We won . . . which meant we would be presented with a cup to keep for the year. This last award – and especially the trophy – was the cherry on top of the cake for us.

One exhibitor was less than pleased, however. As we made our way back, I overheard someone say: 'It's the first time Suffolks have been beaten in the ewe class for twenty years – and to think, we were beaten by a bunch of school kids!' I just wished, at that moment, that we had had a Kerry Hill ram, too, so that we could have won the lot!

We pinned our rosette and prize card on the pen, and the ewes aroused quite a bit of attention. I suppose that was the good side of a breed other than the Suffolks winning. We had many questions from show visitors and other exhibitors. This was the last show of the season, and it was super to finish on a high note.

We decided to increase our flock. We would keep the ewe lambs we had bred and would keep a look-out for a few more. We had already started renting an acre of grass on a neighbouring farm, but if we increased the size of the flock even further it would mean finding another farmer to help us out with suitable pasture.

I was amazed at how much I had learned in just one season. There was still a long way to go, though. I had noticed that the shows tended to bring out the 'characters' in the farming fraternity. In a way, I suppose I was also developing into something of a character on the show scene.

I had learned, too, that there were a few tricks of the trade which the more determined exhibitors would some-times use to help tip the scales in their favour. These were often picked up from other exhibitors, and were passed on in strict confidence – the inner mysteries of the game.

A Kerry Hill sheep should have a white face, with a black patch around each eye and a black patch around the nose. The patches around the eyes should be matching, of course. If they are not, or if the patch is slightly grey or brown, then it is a defect, and a sheep would be marked down because of it. Now I have heard – as it were – that there are those who would seek to 'rectify' such little faults, by unauthorised means. Permanent black hair dye makes a very good job of it, I have been told. This is best applied with an actual paint brush, working it in between the hairs. The dye is left on for 25–30 minutes, to allow the colour to develop. It is massaged gently, and then rinsed off. Any of the black dye running off into a white area must be cleaned off immediately with a sponge or cotton wool. The 'old pros' tell me that if the job is done carefully you just cannot detect it. I would not know of course. . . .

Now if it happens, on the morning of the show, that a sheep has got a few grey or brown hairs in amongst its black markings, this calls for a different approach. Doing a 'paintwork' job on a sheep would certainly be frowned upon, so one has to be discreet. This is where the black mascara comes in. It has to be one of the more expensive brands – one that is waterproof, too. Cheap mascara will rub off onto the halter, and having it rub off onto your lovely white show coat is not a little embarrassing to explain. Sheep with naturally watery eyes are a hazard in this respect. There is nothing worse than a tearful-looking sheep whose mascara has run!

Black patches of wool – instead of the normal colour – is a common fault. One black patch is often to be found in the sheep's neck. To tackle this, first become friendly with a local hairdresser. Then give a piece of normal wool and a piece of black wool to them. Every time a lady comes into the shop to have her hair dyed the hairdresser will experiment with the different blonde shades. Then, when the best colour match has been attained, you can try it on a live sheep. Mind you, you have got to get the shade just right – hence the need for much experimentation. Otherwise, you end up with a worse problem than you had in the first place. I have also heard of bleach being used, too, to eradicate black wool. Again, you will need to do much testing on strands of wool, since the length of time it is left on the wool will affect the end result.

One character actually cut the black wool out of a sheep's neck with his hand shears. This is hardly recommended. In fact, he left a large hole in the coat which obviously showed skin at the bottom. In desperation, he cut a piece of wool from the neck of one of his non-showing animals and tried gluing this back onto his show animal. It looked very good, I am told – until the sheep lowered its head to feed or drink. The rest of the wool parted with the movement, but this false patch just stayed in a big round blob. The judge spotted it and the poor animal was relegated to last place!

One exhibitor urgently needed to wash his ram. The ram had decided to go for a walk under the tractor, and had become covered with grease. He had an old tin bath in the yard, but when he came to fill it up with water he realised it had a hole in it. There just was not time to go out and get another one, so, on impulse, he took his ram upstairs and plonked him in the bath for his wash and shampoo. It was bad enough persuading the poor animal to go upstairs, and get in the bath – but getting him back down, all wet, was even worse. He left a wet trail right through the house – and his wife went mad when she got back. Another example, I fear, of a farmer putting his sheep before his family – a not uncommon plight.

Nowadays, we attend some fifteen agricultural shows each year, and I reckon to travel upwards of about three thousand miles. The local shows have no Kerry Hill breed classes, and so we are showing against all other breeds. At the major shows – and even one or two minor ones on the borders of Shropshire and Powys – there are specialist Kerry Hill classes. Many of these smaller shows are over a hundred miles from home, but if I want to compete against other Kerry Hill breeders I just have to travel. Most Kerry Hill breeders live in the Shropshire/Powys area, and the only occasion they actually travel over to Warwickshire is for the Royal Show – the highlight of the season. I usually jibe them about attending our little 'local show' or, if they give it a miss, tell them it will probably not be held next year, as a result.

Showing is a way of life, you see. It is a bug – and once you have been bitten, you just have to carry on. You certainly do not do it for the money. The entry fees are high and, of course, just the sheer travelling eats heavily into whatever prize money is attained. My poor car will usually be towing a trailer full of sheep and the car itself will be stacked with eager pupils ready to help. I card and trim each show sheep each week which takes a total of eight or nine hours. The faces and legs of the show sheep are washed before each show, then we place straw on the trailer floor and take along with us a bale of hay and a bale of straw. In the car itself we carry the water buckets, feeding bowls, white coats, halters and – if we are feeling confident – drawing pins to pin up the rosettes and prize certificates!

The process of taking the livestock from show to show runs its course through the summer. At the larger shows, the exhibitors will spend perhaps three or four nights sleeping at the show ground. Most sheep exhibitors actually sleep in their stock lorries, landrovers or trailers. It is much handier to be on-site, rather than at a nearby hotel – and most, like me, begrudge the money that would cost! It is all part of the comradeship of the thing, too.

Summer goes on with some disappointments and, hopefully, some moments of triumph. Some you win; some you lose. Occasionally I wonder if there are not better ways of spending the summer months than loading sheep on and off trailers.

You take some orders for stock, of course. Some days, you could sell a lorry load; other days you do not even get an enquiry. It is good for the breed, though. A show is a sort of 'shop window' for the breeders, and those that are keen will skip silaging, haymaking or combining . . . and even leave the wife and kids to be there.

Remember, it is the summer months, and most exhibitors will fight shy of going away on holiday with the family if it means missing an important show. They are likely to weigh up the cost of a family holiday . . . and opt to buy a good-quality ram, instead!

Where There's Muck There's Money!

MANURE HAD become a real problem on our little farm. Now that we were well established we had a large number of livestock in a relatively small area. Our ewes were in-wintered from about the first of January until after lambing in March. They would then go out in the daytime, returning indoors at night, for at least a month. We housed our show team of ewes and rams all the time after they were sheared in December.

As well as all the sheep we had half a dozen calves, two or three goats and four pigs – all housed. We also had numerous small animals, about twenty-four hybrid laying hens, plenty of ducks, geese and rabbits . . . a sort of miniature Noah's Ark, you might say.

They all had one thing in common. They produced prodigious amounts of manure. And it just kept piling up and up.

Our stock was kept cleaner than it would have been on most farms. Effectively, we were on show every day (as the headmaster was constantly reminding me!) and so the straw bedding was not allowed to get dirty. We cleaned out the buildings frequently, too, not letting the manure pile up. As a consequence, the manure we took out was not well rotted when we put it into plastic bags – empty fertiliser bags, in fact.

The pupils sometimes mucked out during rural studies 'practical lessons', or after school and at weekends.

'I held the bag last time, Sir! It's his turn to hold the bag . . .' was the usual comment at such times. The 'plum job' is forking out the manure. The sucker gets to hold the bag, a somewhat dubious pleasure, to say the least. Inevitably some of the stuff ends up missing the bag . . . but

151

almost always connecting with the poor soul holding it. The only way to deal with large lumps is for the person holding the bag to manoeuvre it in by hand. The brown stuff gets all over your hands . . . then dries. They say 'like attracts like' and it is certainly true in this case, because before you know it successive layers of the stuff have built up on your skin to the point where it looks for all the world as if you are wearing a pair of very thick, old and worn-out gloves. The only advantage I have noticed is that it does tend to cure one, very quickly, of the odious habit of nail-biting!

Inevitably there was one exception even to this general rule of hygiene. Daniel was . . . shall we say . . . something of a 'rough diamond'. I have known him muck out the calves, end up with the inevitable 'brown gloves', then sit down and scoff a pound of strawberries he had just bought. At the end of it, though his hands and wrists were still a disconcerting shade of brown, his fingers were beautifully clean! Funnily enough, I never knew him have a day's illness. Must have had a cast-iron stomach.

The kids who do the 'mucking out' on the farm are our local version of the old 'local lepers'. The keen ones will work right up to the end of the lesson, dash out to give their hands a quick rinse under the outside tap, and be off to their next class. Generally they will not have bothered to change out of their school uniform, so they will carry an aroma of the countryside to geography, maths or English. Old Harris, my favourite townie teacher, just loved it. He was always complaining about my 'evil-smelling minions', as he called them. He has even been known to have one of my 'scented sentinels' stand outside in the corridor for the full lesson. A bit much, I think, though the boy himself volunteered for mucking out before the next English lesson! One or two others adopted this ruse to miss English and I even caught one character smearing muck all over his hands and arms and filling up his wellies with the stuff. With the addition of the finishing touch of the inevitable straw in the hair he was ready to do a very passable impression of Worzel Gummidge for old Harris. Says something about the relative delights of English grammar, punctuation and sentence construction. I must tell Harris that, one day. . . .

Not that anyone can tell Harris anything. One day I had a wonderful conversation with him in the staffroom. I was sporting a rather natty new woollen jumper, knitted by an enthusiastic parent from wool sheared from our prize Kerry Hill show ewes.

'Do you like my jumper?' I asked. 'It's from one of our very own Kerry Hill ewes.'

Harris looked at me, somewhat dubiously, over the top of his copy of *The Times*.

'You cruel devil!' he said. 'Fancy killing a sheep just so you can go around . . . er . . . showing off in that thing!'

He went quite red in the face and for once almost seemed lost for words. I certainly was. The man might have two university degrees, but when they were handing out common sense I reckon he got short-changed. Still, back to our manure. . . .

Once the stuff is bagged, we stack it at the bottom of the garden or, if we have enough, load it straight into the trailer. We have to be wary about which way the wind is blowing. The neighbours have complained once or twice, and then I had the pleasure of a 'visitation' from the headmaster, and another lecture on the need to put on a 'good show'. I endured an even greater lecture after one of the neighbours threatened to get the Environmental Health inspectors around. Nor did he really approve of our selling the manure door-to-door. I thought that was rather enterprising, and we were doing a roaring trade ... until someone complained about 'slave labour' and 'how degrading it was to have little Johnny do this kind of thing. . . .' That brought forth the 'image of the school' lecture. One of my favourites, that.

When I have manure to dispose of these days, I stand up at the start of each lesson and do my commercial. I ask the pupils if their parents, or anyone they know, might want some 'garden fertiliser'. I reward my second year 'best salesmen' with much sought-after house points. Unfortunately the delights of house points have worn off by the third and fourth year, and I have to rely on good old enthusiasm to do the trick ... except, that is, for one or two entrepreneurs, who have been known to add on fifteen to twenty pence to the selling price and pocket the difference. I am not supposed to know about that, though.

Our trailer is only an eight-foot, two-beast one – which we regularly overload with bags of manure. I do not have the time (or the inclination) to take it in two loads, so when we hit the road on our muck round the trailer is practically scraping the ground and the bonnet of the car is sticking up in the air.

Mind you, we have got a strange bunch of customers. Some are very helpful and will give us a hand to unload the manure. Others are less than helpful. My least favourite is the man who comes to the front door in his slippers, or in suit and tie, and is obviously not going to 'muck in' (as it were!). You can bet your bottom dollar, too, that he wants it delivered right to the bottom of his mile-long garden, and that we will have to negotiate an obstacle course of clothes lines, ornamental pools, deck chairs and gnomes.

We like to empty the bags, since the customers are

notorious for not returning them. Once, in my enthusiasm, I lifted high the empty bag – forgetting I was close to the washing line – and caught the pair of pink frilly ladies' knickers pegged out to dry. It left a wonderful brown stain, right down the back. I did not have the heart to tell the poor woman.

The other hazard of the job is the bag with the hole in it . . . particularly if you are unfortunate enough to have it full of pig slurry. You leave an interesting trail of wet manure. The only advantage is that the bag is a lot lighter by the time you get to the bottom of the garden.

We have some real characters among our lady customers. My favourite is the one we have nicknamed Margot – after Penelope Keith's character in 'The Good Life'. She lives in an expensive area just round the corner from the school, and when we first called she had kitted herself out in red wellingtons, plastic hat and thick gloves, ready to 'muck in'. We tipped the muck in a heap on the drive, and she tentatively forked it into her dainty little wheelbarrow – not easy with the window-box type fork she was using! She managed half a load, then said it was no good; she felt ill, and would have to go for a lie down!

Some customers are very thoughtful, and will let us wash our hands before we leave. With others, all we get is to wipe our hands on the grass. Then it is a case of driving back to school without touching either seat belt, gear lever or steering wheel; quite a challenge, really.

You have to be a bit crafty about 'the goods'. The allotment holders are the ones – they really know the well-rotted good stuff and will not touch the strawy material. The typical 'townie' housewife has no idea, however, and tends to prefer that 'nice yellow colour'. I will do anything to get rid of the manure, though, and, I must confess, have even been known to switch a bag or two on the unsuspecting customer. The trick is to unload one or two good bags, then, when the customer goes to get the money, do a quick switch with some of the strawy material; a bit naughty but all in a good cause.

When the worst comes to the worst and I cannot sell the muck I have to take it down to Mick's farm and just dump it there. That always breaks my heart; there is no profit in that deal.

This reminds me of when I was working for Mick and he asked me to clean out the cess pit. The pit contained the slurry from the cowshed, from a couple of old-fashioned pig sties, and from the toilet in the house itself. To do the job I had fixed a cow's metal drinking bowl to the end of a large broom handle. This enabled me to scoop out the mess, slopping it into the manure spreader. The work was going well. Mick came to see how I was doing.

'Most farmers get the council to come and empty the cess pit,' I said. 'I don't think much of this job!'

'You've got to be kidding,' said Mick. 'It costs money if the council does it; besides, why should they get all that good-quality manure,' he said, with the evil grin I had got to know only too well.

'Actually, they did come out once,' he continued. 'Two men emptied the cess pit and one of them was stood on top of the full tanker. He'd got his sleeves rolled up and was fishing about in the muck, right up to his armpit. His mate couldn't figure it out, and asked him what on earth he was doing.

' "I dropped my jacket in there," said Paddy.

' "Why worry," said his mate. "The council will give you a new one."

' "I'm not worried about the jacket. It's just that my sandwiches are still in the pocket!" '

Mick walked off, chuckling to himself. He must have thought that I had not heard the joke before; but I had.

I got on with the job, and was on the last lap, scraping the floor clean. I was about to get out of the pit when I heard a funny swishing noise behind me. I turned . . . and got a face-full of water and other materials. Mick or his wife had flushed the toilet. It sure put me off my tea, I can tell you.

Anyway, back to the manure business.

The ideal situation is where the customer comes to collect

the manure. Sometimes the bags go straight into the boot of the car, or even on to the back seat. One day a hot-dog van rolled up and the man loaded twenty bags into it. I have had second thoughts about hot-dogs, ever since. I am sure the Environmental Health Officers would have had a field day.

'Can I have a bag of manure, please, Sir?' asked Kevin.

'Only one bag?' I replied. 'That won't go very far in your large garden.'

'Yes, Sir, but I only want to put it in the bottom of the trench for my runner beans.'

'All right, but it's not worth my while to deliver it. Twenty pence won't even cover my petrol, you know.'

'Oh, that's OK,' said Kevin. 'My dad said he'll pick it up tomorrow, after school. He'll put it in the back of the car for me. Make sure it's good manure, Sir,' he said with a knowing wink. 'I don't want a bag full of straw.'

Cheeky blighter! As if I would.

The day came, and I sorted out the heaviest, smelliest bag I could find. I left it at the corner of the playground for him. Kevin appeared at 3.45 pm, and paid me the twenty pence. He disappeared, and on my way home I just checked that the bag had gone. It had, and I thought no more of it. Not until the next morning, that is.

I happened to be in the secretary's office when the phone rang. She passed the caller on to the headmaster. I do not know why, but I looked up from what I was doing, a sixth sense warning me that something was afoot. I could see that the headmaster was very, very apologetic – not his style, really, and I just had that feeling. . . .

'. . . but how did a bag of manure come to be on the bus?' he asked.

I stiffened, smiled weakly at the secretary, and made for the door. I made the fatal mistake of looking back, and the steely-grey of the headmaster's eyes rooted me to the spot.

'All I can say is that I am most frightfully sorry,' he went on. 'Be assured that I shall get to the bottom of this . . . and those responsible will be punished.' He gave a lot of emphasis to that last word.

In his study he really let fly, asking me what the hell I was playing at letting a boy take manure on to the bus. Was this another of my stupid sales approaches?

Funny, I had never thought of that . . .

I explained the situation, and promised to have a word with Kevin.

'Sort yourself out, man! The reputation of the school is at stake you know and . . .' The lecture went on for another ten minutes – or so it seemed.

I sent for Kevin at the end of the next lesson.

'What happened, Kevin?' He knew what I meant, without elaboration.

'Well, Sir, it was like this. My Dad couldn't pick me up – he had a problem at work at the last minute, so I was stuck. My beans were ready to be planted out, so I got the bus. I put the bag of manure on the rack above my head. I didn't think anyone would notice it there. There were two ladies sitting in front of me, though. One started to sniff the air . . . and looked at the other. Then the second lady started sniffing and looking hard at the first lady. They stared each other out for a good minute or two. Then the first lady – ever so sweetly – said: "Have you got something on your shoe, dear?" The other lady went pink. I thought she would hit her. Anyway, they both started inspecting their shoes – heads down – a bit like our ducks – when the bus braked suddenly. The bag of manure rolled off the rack, spilling some of its contents right on one of the old ladies. I gasped . . . and then she hit me with her brolly. The conductor threw me off the bus – me and the bag. Can you believe, Sir, he wouldn't even refund my fare? I had to walk the last mile with the bag over my shoulder.'

'I suppose you left the bus in a mess, then?' I queried.

'No, Sir!' he replied indignantly. 'I paid good money for that manure and it looked real good stuff, so I scraped it all up with my hands and stuffed it back in the bag!'

There are times in this life when words fail you; this was one of them. I just shook my head, and helped Kevin write

a letter of apology to the bus company. At lunchtime we both went to see the headmaster – safety in numbers, you know. It seemed to work. The headmaster just muttered something about wishing he worked at a 'normal' school, and showed us out.

I remember one boy who bought his father twelve bags of manure for Christmas! I told him that I thought it was a little unusual, and suggested one of our nice potted hyacinths instead. He just could not agree, so I dutifully delivered the twelve bags when dad was out. I had a wonderful mental picture of leaving them under the Christmas tree, all wrapped in nice paper; One bag for each Day of Christmas – sort of 'twelve sacks a-smelling'. Different.

A Mrs Baxter rang me at school: 'Deliver forty bags of manure to my home, please. That's number 66 Park Road. Tip it on the front lawn in a large heap, and my husband will wheelbarrow it into the back garden when he gets home from work.'

'I've got a fifth-year group of lads who can bring it to you in the morning,' I said.

'I'll be in until eleven.'

'The boys will be there at nine-thirty,' I replied, thanking her for the order. Forty bags, and just round the corner, too; magic.

The boys started loading the wheelbarrows at quarter past nine. That would keep them out of mischief, I reckoned, since this was one of my 'less able' classes. To them, too, this was a lot better than writing an essay – real work, as it were. I gave them instructions, and sent them on their way. Off they went, singing 'Hi ho, hi ho, it's off with the muck we go!' I settled down to some serious marking.

Back they came from time to time to re-fill the barrows and take another load. At last, Jeremy came in: 'All done, Sir.'

I looked up from my marking. 'Well done. Did you get the money?'

'No, Sir. She wasn't in, so we just dumped it on the lawn, like you said.'

'OK,' I said. 'I'll call tonight and pick up the ill-gotten gains.' Jeremy looked puzzled.

'Sir?'

'Don't worry, Jeremy. I'll call for the cash.' He looked reassured.

At noon Mrs Baxter phoned. 'You promised to deliver the manure this morning. I've been waiting in, especially.'

'Oh, we have,' I replied chirpily. 'The lads took it round at about nine-thirty – like I said.'

'No they didn't!' she said sternly.

'Er . . . I'll look into it,' I said weakly. I put the phone down, mind racing. It rang again.

'My name is Mr Patterson. I live at number six, Park Road, and I've just come home to find a bloody great pile of manure on my prize lawn. Are you the idiot responsible?'

Mentally, I pleaded guilty on both counts. 'Oh dear,' I said, trying to sound unconcerned. 'My fifth-year lads must have delivered it to the wrong house – how . . . how . . . unfortunate.' I should have searched longer for the word.

When he had calmed down I promised to get round, double-quick, and sort it out.

I had to call in a few favours with the rest of the teaching staff to persuade them to let me have the lads out of lessons. It was just a good job English was not next on the timetable. Old Harris would have loved turning me down. I found someone to take my lesson too, and off we went, wheelbarrows in convoy, trekking off down the road.

Sure enough, on the lawn of number six was the biggest pile of manure I have ever seen, steaming nicely, and with about a million flies in attendance. The wheelbarrow tracks had not improved the lawn, either. Out came Mr Patterson – letting fly with more of the 'verbals'. The boys sniggered appreciatively. I did my best to smooth him down, and we set to work barrowing the manure down to number 66.

Mrs Baxter took over from where Mr Patterson had left off, giving me a right going-over. I trudged back up to number six, head down. By then, Mrs Patterson had arrived on the scene, and I got 'round three' from her. I sent the lads back to school, and did my best to repair the lawn. I told Mrs Patterson that our manure was wonderfully rich in nitrogen, phosphate and potash; she seemed decidedly unimpressed. 'Huh! It's that big brown stain that bothers me,' was her only reply.

An hour later I had brushed most of it off and hosed it down, and it was looking something like a lawn once more.

Back at school Jeremy came to apologise for mixing up the house numbers. 'I thought you said six, Sir, not sixty-six.'

'Why do I bother?' I said dejectedly.

Harris made my day complete. 'What qualifications do you have?' he asked during the afternoon break.

'An MSc,' I replied, confidently.

'What . . . A Master of Science?'

'No. A Muck Shovelling Certificate!'

James Bond Ram

IT WAS TIME to buy a new ram. The old ram was definitely past his best. Not that he lacked any 'enthusiasm', that is, but the performance was not there.

I made some enquiries and a couple of telephone calls, and had success when I telephoned a breeder at Hereford – a Mr Prince. He said I could go up to the farm to purchase a ram and that he had about fifty from which I could choose. I arranged to go to the farm the following Saturday.

I had plenty of eager pupils keen to make the trip with me, so I chose two who had worked hard at weekends and during the holidays. We set off early one September morning. I hitched up the trailer to the car, since I intended bringing the new ram home straight away.

On arrival we were made welcome and given cups of steaming hot coffee. The two pupils – Rachel and Rebecca – were as keen as me to get cracking and sort through the 'candidates'. Ever since I had taken these two girls to have our goat served they reckoned they knew everything about stock!

Two border collies fetched the flock of fifty pedigree Kerry Hill rams into the building. I needed a ram to mate with my ewes to produce lambs we could show. Most of the rams were shearlings, with large black markings on the face, ears set high and upright, a good length and depth to their bodies and good dense-quality fleeces. At first glance they looked excellent – but obviously a very close inspection was called for.

I started to go through them one by one. The poorer-quality rams I immediately caught and turned back out into the field. I enjoy sorting out sheep – one of my favourite

163

jobs, in fact. The two girls helped me catch them, and I told them the things I was looking for as we went through.

'We won't bother with that ram; he's far too small,' I said. 'Catch me another one. No . . . he's not for us. His markings are too pale. Yes, keep him. He looks good . . . except for that bit of black wool in his neck.' The job went on.

I checked the teeth on every ram, and also checked for two testicles. I wanted a ram that was firing on both cylinders. He had important work to do!

Finally, we were down to the last five. Now it was going to get tricky, since all of the remainder were excellent and choosing between them would not be easy. Mr Prince helped, and we narrowed it down to just two. These were very similar – but it was my decision, finally, so I went for the one with the slightly more pronounced facial markings.

'That's him!' I said. 'What do you want for him?' I added nervously.

'Oh, I reckon I could get up to a thousand pounds for him at the Kerry Hill Breed sale at Builth Wells.'

I gulped. That seemed a bit rich. The record price paid for a Kerry Hill ram at that time was nine hundred guineas – and the average price was around two hundred. Certainly, this ram was a cut above the average – but I could not afford a thousand pounds.

'Well, I could not go up to a thousand,' I ventured. 'I'll give you three hundred; that's an above-average price. What do you reckon?'

'No chance!' he replied.

It was looking a bit grim; time for my 'hearts and flowers' routine.

'We're only a school, you know – not a large farm business, and . . .' I gave him my best shot, but he seemed unmoved.

'No. I'll just have to enter him at the sale at Builth Wells.'

Time for my last card. 'Five hundred is my absolute top price. Even if we had more money, I don't think I could justify paying more than that for one sheep.'

'No – I'll put him in the sale; I might get a thousand pounds. He's the best ram I've got, and if I sell the best ram privately other farmers might say I've only bothered to put my second-rate rams in the sale. No, even if you offered me a thousand I wouldn't take it,' he said with an air of finality.

'I'm very disappointed,' I said in my most doleful voice. 'It's very difficult for me to get a day off school, and the sale is on a Monday in school term time.'

There was no budging him, however. We travelled back in silence, all of us disappointed. We had set our heart not just on buying a ram, but on actually bringing him back with us. By the time we were back the petrol gauge was registering empty. I had used twenty pound's worth of petrol on a wild-goose chase.

The following Monday I outlined the situation to the headmaster, requesting that I be given permission to go to the Kerry Hill sale.

'But can't you just take half a day, and buy a ram from some local sale, man?' he queried.

I explained that Kerry Hill rams were rarely sold in our area; that we needed a ram unrelated to our present ewes, for breeding reasons – and that I was sure that the honour and reputation of the school and its breeding flock would be best served by buying a quality animal. I could put the old ram into the same sale, and offset the cost to some extent.

He stroked his chin and looked pensive. 'I can't see the county council paying you to go to a sale,' he said. 'If it was an educational course of some kind, it would be different.'

'But I'll be taking three pupils with me in the car. It will be an educational trip for them,' I ventured.

He brightened a little. 'It would be better if you took a coach full of pupils,' he went on. I was beginning to wonder what I had let myself in for.

'I'll have enough on my hands buying the right ram and getting him home in one piece,' I said. 'A coach full of pupils, too, would be a real problem . . . and what would the coach company say about having a ram on their bus?'

He went a little pale. Our recent exploits with a certain bag of manure and his resulting conversation with the bus company did the trick. I was off the hook with the coach idea. He changed tack.

'But where are you going to get a thousand pounds, man? Am I to mortgage the school, sell off the desks and chairs . . . or have you something else in mind?'

I did not dare say that all of these would be fine by me! I just smiled.

'I'll get there in plenty of time, sort through the rams and pick out second and third choices too,' I said confidently. 'That way we can ensure we don't pay too much.'

'Go ahead,' he said resignedly. 'You win!'

I thanked him very much . . . and left quickly, before he changed his mind.

The day arrived. I planned to take three pupils with me – one boy and two girls – all of whom were very interested in sheep. We met at the school gates at 5.00 am, which meant getting up at 4.00 am – quite an effort for us all. We gave the livestock an 'early breakfast' – and got some funny looks for our pains. I hitched up the trailer and loaded 'Ben', our aged ram. We set off for Mid-Wales.

It was a long journey – and we made it non-stop. We arrived in Builth Wells at a quarter past nine, parked the car and trailer and sought out the pens. All of them were empty. Though we had had such a distance to travel we were seemingly the first there. We put some straw in the pen and unloaded Ben. Then we sat down to our sandwiches and flasks of coffee. The sale did not start until one o'clock, so we had plenty of time to kill.

Just after ten a succession of Land Rovers, trucks and cattle-wagons began to roll in, and the car park began to fill. I noticed two things: only about one in forty of the farmers 'paid and displayed', and another equally rare sight was to see a farmer lock his vehicle.

We obtained a catalogue and noted that our ram was number twenty-four on the sale programme. I had some concerns that this was too early in the sale causing the price to be a little on the low side. Mr Prince arrived late. His rams were penned up, and immediately a whole bunch of farmers mysteriously appeared and in no time at all the pen was packed – like bees around a honey pot. They were poking and prodding – looking at size, teeth, markings and wool. It amazes me that only a few farmers seem to look at the ram's testicles. I reckon this is the first place to check, for a breeding ram. You would not check out a racing car without looking at the engine!

I found the ram we were interested in almost immediately. I had memorised his markings, and he was easy to spot. Unfortunately, though, he was attracting quite a bit of general attention, too. I toured the pens and picked out my next three favourites, just in case the price on our original choice was too high. At local sales butchers have the best idea. They get together beforehand and arrange not to bid against each other, to help keep prices down. Farmers, on the other hand, are very independent creatures. They just plug away at each other, pushing up the price all the time.

However, I checked with Mr Stone and Mr Porter, and

we agreed to do a deal to avoid this problem. As it happened, they were keen to buy my number two choice, so they tossed a coin for it, to decide who would have a clear run. I agreed to stay out of this bidding, provided they left the field clear for me with my number one choice.

When I studied the catalogue further, it became apparent that my favourite animal was practically the last animal for sale that day. I would have to wait ages and, more importantly, would have to decide what to do about my second, third and fourth choices; would I risk all and forego bidding on my other choices to go for this favourite one at the end of the sale?

What a problem. I had travelled all this way, missing a day of school, and all with the prospect of returning home with an empty trailer. The headmaster would have my guts for garters!

The sale ring was in a modern, covered building, and the stockman would go in the ring with the ram to show it off by keeping it moving. The owner would stand in the commentary box, along with the auctioneer, who would tell the prospective buyers all about the animal in question. I had jotted down a few details about our ram, Ben, and passed them to the auctioneer. He certainly did his best. I almost bought the animal myself! Bidding started at fifty . . . and stopped, all too soon, at one hundred guineas. I was shattered. I had expected a fair bit more.

Next in the ring was the ram Mr Porter intended to buy – my number two choice. I looked round the ring for him, but could not pick him out. Someone else bought him, but I thought nothing of it. Perhaps he had asked this man to bid for him, so as not to attract attention; it happens, sometimes.

The illusion was shattered, however, when Porter and Stone came scurrying over to me. They had gone off for a 'quick half' and missed the sale; the ram had gone to someone else. Stone had managed to find the buyer, however, and persuaded him to sell it to him for an additional two hundred pounds. Porter then offered Stone a further hundred, but Stone would not sell! What complications! I just could not see the sense in constantly pushing up the price like that, and hoped I was not going to get involved in such dealings when it came to the time for my purchase.

The day dragged on. All our sandwiches and coffee had long since gone, and the pupils were now beginning to get bored. By four in the afternoon most of the farmers had concluded their dealings, and many were moving out, off home to do the milking. My spirits rose a little; every one that left was one less involved in the bidding for my ram.

At long last the ram that we wanted to buy came into the sale ring. By now there were only about fifty people left at the ringside, and I felt confident. The bidding started at fifty guineas. I came in at sixty, with further bids at eighty and a hundred. My main adversary droppped out and shuffled off, looking disgruntled. My delight was short-lived, however, as another bidder entered the fray. I tried to size him up. He looked as though he had plenty of money, though it is difficult to tell with farmers. At the outset he seemed very determined and I was getting worried. At my bid of 210 guineas there was a lull in the bidding.

'At 210 guineas – are there any more bids? Have you all finished, gentlemen? Are you sure? Going . . . going . . .

'. . . gone to Mr Terry,' he concluded, banging down his gavel.

I had done it, and felt like jumping up and down. And at 210 guineas, too – what a price! All the upsets of the day were forgotten, and we all travelled home with the contentment of a job well done.

'What shall we call him?' asked Janet, a few days later.

'I'm not sure . . . we'll soon think of something,' I replied. I did not want to put him with the ewes for a few days, so I put him in with a young ram lamb that would keep him company. I put them out in the paddock during the daytime, but brought them in at night for security. On the first day I personally shepherded them out across to the left of the greenhouse and into the paddock. This first time they were a bit nervous, but by Wednesday I had them fairly well trained.

I was on playground duty on Thursday morning – a teacher's least favourite task . . . after marking, that is. You have to patrol the playground, quelling the odd riot, helping to prevent bloodshed and mayhem, and generally ensuring that the pupils do not tear each other limb from limb . . . at least before school starts. I always feel a bit like Wyatt Earp, in Dodge City, when I am doing this. Since I was on duty, two of my helpers, Paul and Sid, had taken it into their minds to surprise me, and to take the rams out to the paddock. Unaware of this, I walked over to my mobile classroom, sat down and got ready to mark the register. Suddenly, the door burst open and in stumbled Sid and Paul.

They rushed up to my desk, knocking over some of the smaller lads on the way.

'Mr Terry, Sir, the ram – he's shot straight through the greenhouse, breaking no end of glass,' spluttered Sid.

I was stunned, and just did not respond at first. 'Er . . . what do you mean?' I heard myself say, fighting down the panic. 'Is he all right?'

'Yes, he's OK . . . but he's not done the greenhouse much good!' panted Paul.

By now I was on my feet, and rushing towards the door. 'Come on! Show me where he is.' My stomach was churning round like a cement mixer as I ran across to the greenhouse. It looked as though a bomb had hit it. The front had completely disintegrated. I looked through, to see that the back was in a similar mess. It looked just as though somebody had driven a bulldozer through it. All that I could think was that the ram must somehow have run through the glass at the front, not seeing it, then panicked and shot out the back. There was glass everywhere, but I just did not have time to think about that. Where was the ram? I had visions of him cut to ribbons, bleeding to death.

I rushed round to the paddock. There he was, standing at the top end, looking a right sight. He had bits of trailing geranium on his head and neck, and all down his back were fragments of fuchsia, chewed-up African violet, ladder fern and begonia. He looked like a very bedraggled Queen of the May. His face was black with potting soil and peat, and there was a veritable trail of broken pots, potting soil and plants littering his route to the top of the paddock. We just stood and stared at each other for a moment or so.

I was relieved to see that he was all in one piece, however. 'Why on earth did you let these two sheep out?' I bellowed at the boys.

'We wanted to surprise you, Sir,' was the timid reply.

'Well, you certainly did that!' I snapped. 'Do you realise the trouble I went to getting that ram?' I went on and on. They were close to tears by now, and I relented a little.

'Sorry, Sir,' said Paul, in a sobbing voice.

'Come on. Let's catch him then. Don't just stand there.'

Easier said than done. The ram was scared out of his wits, and would not let us near him. Up close, he looked even funnier – a bit like a paratrooper out on a night raid, with blackened face and camouflage. Finally we got him rounded up, and headed him and the ram lamb past the shattered remains of the greenhouse, back into the building where they were housed. I was still a little concerned about any cuts I might find under his wool. The first job, though, was to remove the foliage still stuck to him. Embedded in his wool were literally thousands of tiny slivers of glass. It took me ages, but I picked out all the glass and examined him meticulously, from head to toe. His only injury was a cut of about a quarter of an inch long on his nose. Even there, the skin was only just broken. He must have a charmed life, I thought.

I applied terramycin to his face, and then gave him another once-over. Nothing. He really was unscathed. I could not believe my luck. I returned him to the paddock, and then the boys and I erected some rough and ready fencing around the greenhouse to prevent a repeat performance. The boys still looked awful. Glancing at my watch I saw that it was now nine-thirty, and I still had not marked the register. I rushed back to see that my form had gone off to assembly without me. Only a day or so earlier I had received yet another lecture from the headmaster about 'showing the flag' and always being there for assembly. I had tried to explain that there were stock to feed, but there are none so deaf as those who will not hear . . . I was going to be in his bad books again. I think he had a volume just for me!

I took a closer look at the greenhouse. The ram must have shot through there at about 90 miles an hour. There were plants, pots and soil everywhere; everywhere they should not be, that is. My cash register mind was clocking up the tally of the damage done, but soon reached 'overload'. He had even run straight into the greenhouse heater which now lay outside on its back, still plugged in, and blowing hot air out into the paddock.

Still, the fact that the ram itself was unharmed had lifted my mood a little, and the boys sensed it.

'We should call the ram James,' pronounced Sid.

'Why's that?' I asked.

'After James Bond – 007 – you know, Sir. He can dive through windows and things and not get hurt, too!' added Sid.

James Bond Ram

'Perhaps he did it 'cos his lady loves Milk Tray,' said Paul.

I nodded; not yet able to smile, but feeling a little better, at least. To think, health food fanatics were now saying that sheep meat can give you heart attacks. Well, I had nearly had a heart attack, but caused by a live sheep, not a dead one! This ram was taking years off my life. My old boss, Mick, would have recommended a lie down, a cup of tea . . . and a fairy cake.

My class arrived for their rural studies lesson. I gave them a textbook each, and they were told to make notes. I sent Sid and Paul off to their maths lesson, and then picked two of my most reliable pupils and sent them out to patch up the greenhouse, as best we could, with some polythene sheeting. I was concerned about the cold getting to the plants which remained. After that we began to sort through the debris.

For the next few days I continued to put the rams out during the day, returning them to the building at night. I planned to introduce James to his new 'girl friends' late that Saturday afternoon. I bought a new sire harness and crayons for the ram. The ram wears the harness, which holds a crayon. When he serves a ewe, the crayon leaves a coloured mark on the ewe's back, telling the farmer that he needs to make a note in the farm diary, counting forward the 147-day gestation period.

On the Saturday morning I fitted James with the harness and crayon, loaded him into the trailer, and took him to the rented field where we kept our sixteen sheep. I backed the car and trailer into the field. He was looking out of the flaps in the trailer and, when he spied the ewes, he made a very deep baa-ing noise – the first time I had ever heard him make any sort of sound. Within seconds his top lip was curled; a sure sign that he was interested. I could not get the back of the trailer down fast enough for him. I was sure he was going to run through that, too. As the timber back dropped he did a very passable impression of a greyhound leaving its trap, and hurtled across the field in the direction of the unsuspecting ewes.

He sniffed each ewe in turn, with top lip curled back – just to show them who was boss. The next day he served one, and the day after that, another. I felt quite reassured. I remembered reading in a magazine that one stockholder had paid good money for a ram – thousands of pounds, in fact – only to find that he was not the slightest bit interested in ewes!

All went well until a couple of days later when I was telephoned by a Mr Finney, a neighbouring farmer.

'Your bloody Kerry Hill ram is in with my Border Leicester ewes! Come and fetch him out!'

I sought out the deputy headmaster, explained my plight, and he arranged for staff to cover my lesson periods. Within twenty minutes I was up there. Sure enough, old James was giving them a real good going over, sniffing each ewe, and running round like a wild thing. By the time I got there he had served two already . . . and was game for more, if the old top lip was anything to go by. Try as we might, Mr Finney and I just could not catch him – not while the ewes were there at least – so we drove the ewes indoors and then sorted him out. He was most upset. Sixteen ewes were all right . . . but fifty were better.

'What are you going to do about the two ewes he's served?' queried Mr Finney. 'I was just flushing the ewes, ready to put them to our Suffolk ram. My ewes are tremendous fit – and now your ram has gone and upset my plans.' He did not sound pleased.

'Tremendous fit' was one of his favourite expressions – as with many farmers, seeking to praise up their stock. I knew that he sold his 'tremendous fit' lambs to the butcher, and that a Suffolk cross Border Leicester lamb will usually be ready for the butcher before a Kerry cross Border Leicester. He had some concern that the lambs sired by my Kerry Hill would be slower to mature.

'If the ewes produce lambs that are not as big, or if they don't do as well as the other lambs, I'll pay you some compensation,' I said generously.

'Fair enough,' said Mr Finney, relaxing a little.

I felt guilty at the time, patched up the fence with some brand-new sheep netting . . . and then forgot all about the incident.

One hundred and forty-seven days later – to the day – my phone rang very early in the morning. The ringing awakened me, though I would never have admitted that to a member of the farming fraternity – early risers that they are.

'It's Mr Finney here,' said the distant voice. 'One of our ewes has lambed.'

'Very nice,' I said, wondering just what this earth-shaking news had to do with me. Then the penny dropped, and I knew what was coming next.

'We've got twins,' he continued. 'They've got black patches around their eyes and noses and have black and white ears and legs. It's pretty obvious who the father is!' He was speaking accusingly – as though I, personally, was somehow responsible!

I tried to smooth things over, but he was obviously upset. At lunchtime I drove up to the farm to see the lambs. They were big and strong. If they had been mine, I would have been pleased.

The next day, Mr Finney rang again. 'We've got a big single ram lamb this time,' he said.

Again, I went up to the farm to inspect the latest arrival. Boy, he was a big one. He looked more like a Kerry Hill than a border Leicester, and must have weighed a very respectable fifteen pounds. I checked on the twins, and they were doing fine, too. However, Mr Finney still seemed neither impressed nor enthusiastic.

I telephoned him again some three weeks later. 'How are the lambs?' I asked.

'Oh, tremendous fit,' he replied.

'Do you mean you don't mind them?' I queried.

'No . . . I must admit they are very good, strong lambs; born with no trouble at all, and drinking from their mothers far quicker than a Suffolk cross.'

'That's the hardy hill characteristic coming out,' I said.

175

'Do I owe you any compensation?'

'No,' replied Mr Finney, in a tone which betrayed the fact that he had mellowed considerably.

'Oh, in that case I was wondering when I could expect to receive my stud fee?' I asked.

There was a stunned silence at the end of the line for about ten seconds, then a string of abuse. I did not press the point.

I was very pleased, too, with the pedigree Kerry Hill lambs we produced. We kept some ewe lambs for showing and breeding; we also retained a couple of ram lambs for showing before selling them to other breeders.

James Bond had literally made his mark on our ewes, and did the look of the flock proud. He really was quite a lad! I must say he made his mark on Mr Finney's flock, too. Mr Finney kept his two Kerry Hill cross Border Leicester ewe lambs for breeding purposes, and put them to a Suffolk ram.

I was talking to him one day, and he remarked on what good mothers they made.

'That's the characteristic of the hardy hill breed,' I proudly declared. 'That reminds me, I never did get that stud fee.'

The air went blue!

Money!

THE RURAL STUDIES funds were very low indeed, threatening to put a stop to future developments. So far we had reason to feel proud of what we had been able to accomplish in a relatively short time. Take the wooden building; we had built this over a period of three years, building one bay each year. We dug out the soil and replaced it with rubble, put down a layer of sand, with a paving slab floor on top. We built the sides, making wooden frames out of 2 inch square timber, and then nailed on matchboarding. The upright posts were concreted into the ground, and the sections were bolted together. We had large beams supporting the roof, which was corrugated metal sheeting. We even made the doors ourselves – with no help whatsoever from Mr Petty, the woodwork teacher. Despite him warning darkly about 'amateurs' trying to do 'professional' work, we did it . . . and they were fine.

Each bay measured 12 feet by 24 feet and the building looked much more professional than our first effort in this area – the old bicycle shed we had built back in 1974. A fourth bay – somewhat larger than the others – would finish the building off nicely. We could make this 15 feet by 24 feet, making a total length of 51 feet. I planned, then, to make a walk-through feeding passage, 3 feet wide, running the length of the building. This we would make from galvanised hurdles, and in each bay one hurdle would have a gate built into it which would enable you to walk into that section.

This extension was very much on my mind. Every time I looked at the existing building I started thinking about that planned fourth bay. Like the rest, it would be a dual-purpose building, housing calves, goats, poultry or in-wintered ewes. It would really finish things off, and there was only one obstacle in our way. Money!

Once again our bank account only had about five pounds in it. It was 1981 and our various agricultural and horticultural enterprises were doing well, but we had spent quite heavily, and it was going to be a while before we would get any measurable return on this. We were rearing four pigs a term, buying them as weaners and selling them as half-pigs, for freezers. In the autumn we bought one-week-old calves, selling them at six months old. We were selling goat's milk, goat kids, lambs, rabbits, eggs, ducks, geese and bantams. On the horticultural side, we sold bedding plants, geranium cuttings, vegetables and fruit. Despite this, though, the livestock seemed to be eating us out of house and home. Even feed bought by the ton to get the best price is still very expensive.

We had cut a few corners. A local chemist came to our aid by giving us a quantity of out-of-date baby food ... which we fed to the pigs. They loved it – more than babies do. The pupils took great delight in 'piggy menu-planning', and were very correct about the whole business. In the mornings, it was the breakfast varieties, and in the evening the meaty dishes and stews. They even had puddings! The only problem was that when we finally ran out of the baby food and went back to pig meal, the pigs would hardly touch the stuff; definitely a come-down for them!

Coincidentally, the chemist rang me to ask how the pigs were getting on with the baby food.

'Fine,' I said. 'They just can't get enough of it. The only problem is that we've run out, and they're literally turning their noses up at pig meal.'

The chemist just laughed. Two days later he rolled up with a whole estate car full of apple-flavoured baby food. They lived on this for weeks, and never seemed to tire of it. By the time they were slaughtered at eighteen weeks we had the only pork in Britain which did not need apple sauce on it. It came ready flavoured!

Even so, we were paying out a fortune in feed, and the question of how we were going to raise some extra cash was really taxing my mind. It seemed that all my traditional options had already been cornered: the school's Duke of Edinburgh Award scheme were mad keen on jumble sales; the headmaster was 'big' on sponsored walks. He held them for everything. I sometimes thought that he even organised sponsored walks . . . to finance sponsored walks. The PE department were into aerobics, and ran stacks of discos. It did not leave me many angles, unfortunately. I calculated that I would need about five hundred pounds to build the shed, with another four hundred for the galvanised hurdles and gates. Where on earth was it going to come from?

The pigs had been eating around sixteen pounds worth of out-of-date baby food a day, working on a normal shop selling price of 70–80 pence per box. I looked at the stock I had left, and even wondered, fleetingly, if any of my friends with babies would want to buy a job lot! I weighed it up, but my conscience got the better of me and I had to reject it. Back to the drawing board.

Poultry could be the answer, I thought. I visited a large local poultry farm owned by Derek Crawford. They bought in chicks, day-old, and killed them at 8–12 weeks old, selling them as plucked and dressed birds to local butchers. I looked at the logistics of the operation, and even thought about going into competition with them. In the end I decided that it would be best just to pluck and dress the birds. We would pack them nicely into bags, weigh them . . . and clean up!

I put the idea to my fifth-year pupils. The squeamish ones were not at all keen, but ninety per cent thought it was a good idea, given that we had a significant sum of money to raise.

'We'll start with twenty-four birds,' I announced. 'Then we'll see how it goes from here. What do you reckon: should we buy them with their feathers on, or go for plucked birds?'

'My dad can help!' exclaimed Michael.

'Good,' I replied. 'Has he got a plucking machine?'

'No, Sir . . . but he crossed a cockerel with a guitar.'

I looked puzzled.

'Well, he's got a chicken which plucks itself!'

The class roared with laughter; I did too. I had not heard that one before. Michael was becoming our class comedian, taking over from Steven Wood and Gary Walker, both of whom had left by this time.

I must say that buying them killed, but not plucked, was attractive. We would make a lot more money that way. I had visions of feathers flying around the playground, though, and could just visualise how the headmaster would react to that. In such cases, discretion was decidedly the better part of valour. We agreed to buy them plucked.

We would have to pick them up from Mr Crawford. Then we would take off the head and feet, remove the insides, sort out and bag the giblets, and present the birds all nicely weighed and labelled, in a plastic bag. It sounded fine, and in next to no time I had twenty-four potential customers.

I called for the birds on Thursday morning, before school.

'I've come to collect the chickens,' I announced.

'Is it twenty-four long-legged birds you want?' queried Mr Crawford.

'Oh no. Just the normal length leg will do,' I replied in all seriousness, while everyone else laughed.

'No . . .' said Mr Crawford. 'Let me explain. Long-legged birds are birds which have been killed and plucked, but still have their legs, feet, head and insides intact. Birds are 'oven-ready' on the other hand, when the bottom part of their legs have been cut off, and they have been cleaned.'

'Oh yes. I knew that but, er . . . didn't know the trade term for it,' I said, smiling weakly. Mr Crawford must have thought me a real fool, and it took me about six months to live it down.

I used the birds to demonstrate to my pupils how to prepare a bird for the oven. Some volunteered to have a go and seemed to enjoy it; others were somewhat more reticent. To me, it seemed ideal; here I was, combining education with profit! When we had done, the chickens looked very professional. I felt pleased, and so were the customers.

The following Monday I started to take orders for more chickens. They were going like hot cakes, and soon I had orders for thirty-six. We collected, packed and despatched them, and by the following week I had all the money collected in. It was beginning to mount up and I was celebrating. The next week was even better – forty-eight birds! We even topped that, though, with seventy-two birds the following week, and a massive eighty-four went in the week after that. I could not believe it.

Mr Crawford could not believe it either. 'Eighty-four? You must be joking. That's more than I sell to Dewhursts and the Co-op!'

By now, though, the novelty was wearing off. I was spending every spare moment I had dressing chickens. Then sales began to fall. The project was losing its appeal, and needed a shot in the arm. What could I do to keep the money rolling in?

I had a brainwave. House points! Our younger pupils are awarded house points for such things as good class work, homework, helpfulness and form activities. That was it. I would use the 'system' to give my chicken-selling a much-needed boost.

'Any pupil who sells two chickens will get one house point,' I announced to my class.

'Great!' a wave of appreciation swept round the room. I gave them a fortnight's notice, and we agreed that we would award house points each Thursday. They were really keen. Pupils in the first few years will 'kill' for house points. As they get older they become a little cynical, and you have to find more subtle ways of influencing them.

Did it work! At the end of the fortnight we had sold 203 birds. One girl sold thirty-three, single-handed, and the runner-up sold twenty-five. I could not believe it. Mr Crawford was amazed when I told him. 'I'll end up a millionaire, if this goes on,' he said. 'You're working wonders for my turnover figures.'

It took me two car journeys to bring the chickens back to school. I worked it out: in total, they weighed one thousand and nine pounds, almost half a ton. I got down to work with my volunteer team of pupils, and we prepared some fifty birds before school that morning. I had to give assembly a miss, and one or two of my 'star' packers did likewise. Even

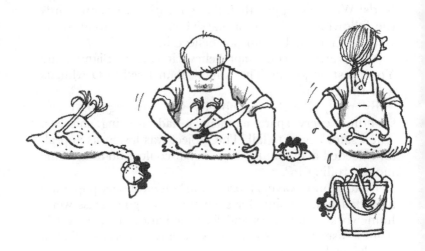

182

so, we were falling behind. I set my first class some written work to do . . . and then did some more packing at the back of the room. I had to enlarge my work force, though, and sent rather blood-splattered notes to some of the teachers, asking if they could release certain pupils to help me. They looked like gruesome ransom notes.

My best chicken 'gutters' were six fifth-year pupils – three boys and three girls. Most of the staff, apart from Harris of course, agreed to release the pupils.

'I know how we can deal with these birds quickly,' announced Michael.

'How?' I asked, somewhat impatiently.

'Well, my dad goes shooting.'

'What's that got to do with it?' I snapped.

'He's just invented a sage and onion bullet, so that he can shoot them and stuff them at the same time!'

Everyone groaned, but it did help to lighten the mood. I got my 'gutters' moving, and we soon had a pile of birds done. I then roped in a few 'volunteers' from my lessons to wash them, and I spent the whole of the day at the back of

the classroom weighing the birds. Then my neatest writers labelled the birds with the customer's name and the weight of the bird.

That was quite a day. Most of my classes spent their time doing written work, I am afraid – but I was coining the money in for my building. I worked through breaks; I worked through lunchtime; everything else came to a halt while we strove to clear the chicken mountain. By four o'clock in the afternoon we had won. They were all sold . . . and we made a handsome profit.

The chicken numbers dropped considerably the next week, but I was happy to let it go. There was no way we could keep that up . . . not without closing the school and going into chicken packing full time, that is. I fleetingly toyed with running that past the headmaster, but thought better of it.

We now average about twenty birds a week, and can live with that. I have also had to 'diversify' a little. The great chicken bonanza could not last forever, so I turned my attention to other possible markets. As part of the CSE course the pupils had planted hyacinth bulbs, three to a pot, in October, planning to sell them at Christmas. We managed sixty pots in all. I wondered what else we could do for Christmas. I toyed with the idea of Christmas trees, but the trouble was that I would have to buy them, and you always run the risk of being left with the unsold ones. A Christmas tree in January is about as much use as a chocolate tea-pot!

I looked into turkey-selling. I think Mr Crawford thought he was on to another winner – but in the event, orders were slow in coming . . . and I could not pull my house points trick a second time. I needed a new 'line', something seasonal . . . and something with a good return. We decided to try Christmas wreaths – the sort that people hang on their front doors for decoration. They are sometimes called 'Christmas knocker-rings'. I bought the special wire frames, a large bag of moss and some binding wire from a local florist's shop . . . at cost price, of course. As it happened, the proprietor was Alan Robinson. He was a former pupil who had been very involved in our rural studies work, so he was keen to co-operate.

I bought some tinsel, baubles, ornaments and ribbon from Woolworths (after checking that no former pupil worked there, too) and had plenty of laurel, holly and conifer growing in the school garden. It was looking good.

The first job was to cover the wire frames with moss. This provides a foundation for the evergreen leaves. The leaves are then bound to the moss; half the leaves being put on in a clockwise direction, and the other half, anti-clockwise. At the bottom we wired the red ribbon, baubles and tinsel. The first one – our prototype – looked pretty amateurish. We had not covered the frame with sufficient leaves. It looked as though it was going bald.

The next day I had to mark fifth-year exam papers, so did not have time to look at the wreath-making again. When I did get back to it I had no more luck. It was difficult to get the ends of the holly and the conifer to overlap, and it just looked messy. I had a word with the art mistress, and roped in a couple of fifth-year girls who were good at arts and crafts. They set to, making one each.

The girls were very good, and soon had two wreaths finished. They were excellent, but time was running out. We had orders for twenty, with two made – but only two days left before we broke up for the Christmas holiday. The trouble was that they were altogether too complicated. Our two nimble-fingered girls could manage them, but the rest of my fifth-form lot had the subtlety of a steam-roller. I did not fancy our chances . . . not without a change of plan.

It was a passing funeral which gave me the idea. Wreaths for funerals would be an altogether different proposition. They would be much easier to make, and we could cut out the tinsel and baubles. I phoned Alan Robinson. He seemed enthusiastic and agreed to buy twenty-five. We were in business.

During my fourth-year lesson, that afternoon, we made a start. Each pupil was given one wreath to make, and in a short time you could not see the desks for the foliage and all the rest of the bits and pieces. I appreciated it was not the jolliest of tasks, but an atmosphere of gloom seemed to have settled over the classroom.

'Sir, are the people that we are making these wreaths for dead yet?'

That one stumped me. 'I don't know ... but keep on working. We've got a deadline to meet,' I quipped. Everyone groaned.

'My Grandad died on Tuesday, Sir. I bet my Mum would buy one of these off you,' remarked one of the pupils.

By now even I was feeling a bit guilty. I must be the only school teacher in Britain getting the pupils to make funeral wreaths. What would the headmaster say? At that moment, I glanced out of the window to see the headmaster marching briskly across the playground towards us. Well, they do say 'speak of the devil ...' I leapt out of my seat, and shot out of the classroom to try and head him off. I intercepted him about twenty yards away from the classroom. I ran just past him, stopped, and so made him turn round, so that his back was towards the spectacle of my wreath-making factory.

'I've got some good news for you, Mr Terry,' he beamed. 'The county council is going to decorate your classroom.'

'Splendid,' I said, with a distinct lack of enthusiasm. It was due for a lick of paint .. but the timing was awful. My mind was racing, trying to come up with some ploy to divert his attention from my classroom. What if he wanted to go in, now, and start working out the colour scheme? The thought filled me with dread. Suddenly, a window opened in the main school building and the school secretary leaned out:

'Headmaster. You are wanted on the phone ... urgently.'

'Oh ... sorry ... I'll have to go,' said the headmaster, excusing himself.

'Oh, no. Think nothing of it!' I said, beaming brightly. He looked slightly puzzled, but returned to his office.

At the end of the lesson period most of the wreaths looked

pretty good. I had our 'experts' touch-up a couple of the unsatisfactory ones – done by some of our rugby-playing fraternity. I loaded them on to the back seat of my car and took them up to Alan's shop after school. I must have looked like a one-man funeral procession. Alan was very pleased with them and gave me a good price. I even sold back to him the moss and the wire he had let us have.

'Would you like to make some more in January?' he asked.

'No, thanks. I don't think I could stand the strain,' I replied, telling him of my close shave with 'he who must be obeyed'. Alan grinned.

On the way back to school – quite a bit richer – I had to smile to myself. I thought about going into business running a teacher-based funeral service – a sort of package deal. As the 'digging department' we would have no trouble with the graves; we could make the wreaths . . . and even have old Petty, the woodwork teacher, making coffins. Miss Perrin, the home economics teacher, could lay on a nice post-funeral spread, and we could get Mr McDougall, the RE teacher, to read the bible and say the prayers. I wondered if Mr Searle, the metalwork teacher, would let us use his forge if people fancied cremation rather than burial. . . . The headmaster could even get in on the act. He had the expression of an overworked undertaker most of the time anyway!

'Did you sell all the wreaths,' asked Judith, my best wreath-maker, when I returned to school.

'Yes. All sold,' I replied.

'Will you be buried or cremated, when you die, Sir?' she asked.

'Cremated,' I replied, somewhat puzzled.

'And what will happen to your ashes?' she asked.

'Oh, I'll state in my will that it will be my last wish to have them scattered over . . . the school vegetable plot!' I replied.

'Yes,' she smiled, 'You must have spent many happy hours on that plot, already.'

'Well, it must be done properly, though,' I said with a straight face. 'I shall leave strict instructions that the ashes are to be forked in, lightly, at the rate of one and a half ounces per square yard!' Now it was her turn to look puzzled.

Our bank account was looking altogether healthier again. The turkeys were our next project. I picked them up from Crawfords on Christmas Eve, and with three volunteers started getting them ready for the oven. During the afternoon the customers collected their birds, and it was only late in the afternoon that we realised we were one bird short. We had bought fifteen birds – but had sixteen customers. When Mrs Yates came in I explained that we had a 'slight technical hitch', but that I would bring her bird round that evening. I then telephoned Crawfords, to be told that they were completely sold out.

'I've got a goose,' said Mr Crawford. 'Is that any use to you?'

I contemplated the situation, but not even I could get a goose to look and taste like a turkey. I thanked him, put the phone down, and left the pupils in charge whilst I sped off into town. I was sure I could pick up a spare bird from a local butchers.

I drew a blank at my first shop. They were sold out, this near to Christmas. The second butcher had just one fresh bird left:

'You're in luck,' he said. 'It's my very last bird.'

When he brought it out I could see why. It looked a bit like an albatross, and weighed a mere twenty-eight pounds! Since Mr and Mrs Yates were pensioners, living alone, they would still have been eating it in June!

'Are you absolutely sure you've got nothing smaller?' I queried.

'Sorry, mate, but you've cut it a bit fine, you know,' replied the butcher.

The next shop could not help . . . nor the next two. By this time the shops were all putting up the shutters – and I was still a turkey short. In the very last shop, tucked away off the main street, I struck gold:

Money!

'Yes, I've got just one fresh turkey left,' replied the shop-assistant. 'It's a twelve-pound oven-ready bird.' Great! I paid for it, and rushed off back to school, feeling somewhat relieved. I was pleasantly surprised to see that I had paid ten pence a pound less for it than I was charging. I took it out of the butcher's bag, re-bagged it into one of ours, and stuck on the customer's name and bird weight label. Finally, I stuck a price tag on it . . . adding 10p a pound over the cost price, of course! Then I delivered it.

Believe me, I took it easy that Christmas holiday. All our scheming and working had left me shattered. After Christmas Mrs Yates telephoned me to say that it was the best turkey she had ever had, and could she please order another one, now, for next year?

It had all been worthwhile, though. I worked out that we had now got enough for our building extension. We built it in the same manner as the earlier sections, with the pupils and myself working during the half-term. Again, we made the doors ourselves. Old Petty was getting really aggrieved. We were getting too good at it. We put in our walk-through, and when it was all finished we were pleased with the results of our efforts.

You know, every time I am working in that building I cannot help thinking how it came about. Building it was easy; raising the money was the difficult part.

Royal Show

MY SECOND show season was 1982. I realised that we had an exceptional pair of Kerry Hill ewes, called Hazel and Katy. They were very large ewes, with a good length and depth to their bodies, good wool, excellent black and white markings, and good upright ears. All in all, they were a well-matched pair – and I had high hopes for them.

We took them to the Three Counties Show, at Malvern, Worcestershire, in early June. For the first time at a major show other exhibitors were looking at our two ewes with real interest. I overheard one man comment: 'These will take some beating' . . . and tried not to let it go to my head!

It was warm and sunny on the day of the judging – a lovely early summer morning. One of our regular helpers, Adam, was helping me with the showing, and the judge took his time in his examination and reflection. Then, to our astonishment and delight, he told us to move the sheep to the top of the line. The penny dropped: we were being moved into first place!

We took our new position with some pride – but not without some concern. Mr Porter and his two ewes were in second position. I looked them up and down. Would the judge change his mind, and reverse the order? The suspense was killing, but finally the judge signalled the steward . . . and we were presented with an enormous silver Challenge Cup for First Prize and Champion Female Kerry Sheep in the show. I was delighted; this was our very first major trophy.

We were real celebrities. The reporter from *Farmer's Weekly* hustled over, interviewed us, and took photographs of the ewes. They seemed to like all the attention even better than we did. True enough, in the livestock section of the following Friday's edition there was a photograph of the ewes with the headline: 'Teenagers teach the old masters at the Three Counties'. The article went on to talk about our farm and garden enterprise.

On the following Monday morning I was hard at work at my desk when the sound of footsteps coming rapidly across the playground caused me to look up. I was totally unprepared for the sight that met my eyes: the headmaster, running across towards our classroom. Funny, but my whole past life seemed to pass before me in an instant. Had the pigs escaped again? Was the school on fire . . . or had the sheep got out . . . ?

The door burst open, and in rushed a somewhat puffed and red-faced headmaster. Struggling to regain his breath, he gasped: 'Mr Terry. You are wanted, immediately, on the telephone.' The emphasis he gave to 'immediately' was ominous. World War III, at the very least.

'Er . . . who is it?' I ventured.

'A reporter from Central Television,' he snapped. 'Come on, man, we're going to be famous. You need to get a move-on. Go on, I'll look after your class.'

I just stood there, rooted to the spot. Shocked as I was by the news that a television reporter wanted to speak to me, that did not come anywhere near the trauma occasioned by the headmaster actually volunteering to take my class!

'Come on, man. Move!' he snapped, bringing me back to my senses. The whole class seemed shell-shocked, too. Thirty faces were all facing us, wide-eyed.

'Get on with your work!' barked the headmaster. I turned and hurtled off towards the main building.

I reached the office and, fighting for my breath, managed to gasp a somewhat strangulated 'Hello?'

'Central TV, here. We are planning coverage for the four afternoons of the Royal Show,' said the voice at the other end of the line. 'We plan to cover the show jumping, agricultural machinery, livestock, rural crafts and . . . oh . . . the flowers, too. We've read the *Farmer's Weekly*

191

article, and would like to come out and do some filming at the school farm.'

'Well . . . er yes . . . ,' I stumbled. 'What exactly did you want to see?'

'We thought the children working with the animals might be nice – you know, the sheep, pigs, poultry and rabbits – that type of thing. We could film your preparations for the show, too – what you need to do with the sheep to prepare them for the big day. We would also like to film you showing the sheep at the Royal Show. If you do well, then we'll have the footage on the sheep we need; if it doesn't work out for you, then we'll concentrate instead on the school farm aspect. How do you feel about that?'

The question presupposed that I was 'feeling' at all. As it was, I was numb, with a million and one ideas flashing around inside my brain, like bluebottles in a jar.

'Splendid,' I heard myself say. 'When did you plan to come?' The arrangements were made for the afternoon of the following Friday.

I could not wait to see my pupils' faces . . . especially Janet, Stephen and Adam. They were the sheep 'specialists'. When I got back to the classroom and broke the news, they were ecstatic. The headmaster was all smiles, too. 'Good for the image of the school,' he kept repeating, absentmindedly.

We got started, straightaway, 'whitewashing the coal' – just as we do when any important visitors are to come. Gardens were weeded, hedges trimmed, gates painted, and the duck pond was cleaned out. The livestock did not know what had hit them. We worked before school, after school, through breaks and through lunch hours. We had 'visitations' from the headmaster at regular intervals to check on progress. Finally, it was done. Everything looked just fine. We had come a long way in eight years, I reckoned, surveying the scene.

The area of wasteland I had inherited for our farm was now transformed. Directly outside the classroom window lay a neat lawn, bordered by roses and herbaceous gardens. In the centre of the lawn was a fish pond, with a rockery close by. Our vegetable garden was well stocked with potatoes, beetroot, parsnips, carrots, swedes, turnips, onions, beans, cabbage, cauliflowers and brussels sprouts. We had an orchard with apples, pears, plums, raspberries, gooseberries, blackcurrants and blackberries, and a greenhouse well stocked with tomatoes, geraniums, fuchsias and African violets.

The duck pond, because of its rather 'unorthodox' construction, could claim to be the strongest in Britain (even if a certain motorway bridge was not), and the three grass paddocks for the sheep and the brick building for the pigs looked a treat. To cap it all, we now had a distinguished show team of pedigree sheep.

The large wooden building we had constructed housed goats, calves, laying hens and rabbits. We had built up a stock of equipment, including a livestock trailer, motor mowers, incubators, food troughs, hay racks, buckets . . . and a host of other bits and pieces. We had come a long way, indeed.

In teaching terms, we were on the map, too. Each second- and third-year pupil took one lesson of rural studies a week – and it was an increasingly popular option when it came to 'make your mind up' time for the fourth- and fifth-year pupils. Students could go on to take CSE and GCE 'O' level examinations, too.

Looking back, it had been hard, but I had enjoyed every minute of it. Well . . . almost every minute. A win at the 'Royal' would be the crowning glory. Could we really win . . . ? I drifted off into reflection. I had to be realistic. Fairy-tale ending though it would be, I did not think we stood much chance, realistically.

On the morning of Central TV's visit I turned up at school wearing (for once) a white shirt, new tie, and a new pair of highly polished shoes. As if that was not enough, I took the three-piece suit out of mothballs. I got some funny looks from various members of the staff – old Harris, in particular – and some decidedly uncouth comments from certain of the older pupils.

'Are you getting married this morning?' shouted Harris sarcastically.

I smiled, albeit through clenched teeth.

'Going for an interview, then, John?' asked Jim Winters, the French teacher.

'You're not after my job, are you? I haven't seen you look as smart as that since September 1974,' said the headmaster, cuttingly. My smile was wearing a little thin by now.

The old jungle drums had been out, and the school was agog with the news of the impending visit by the TV people. Some of the staff amused themselves by running a book on how long it would be before I got sheep muck on my suit.

The Central team arrived on time, at 1.30 pm. The reporter was Paul Baines, and with him was a cameraman, sound engineer and a man who looked after the lighting. They walked around the department with me, to map out what they would film. Twenty minutes later I was being filmed teaching my fourth-year class about showing sheep. Then they interviewed a number of the pupils, asking them about the livestock in general and the sheep in particular.

Outside they filmed groups of pupils working with the pigs, feeding the calves, milking the goats, and so on. This was the first time any of us had had such an experience – and we were lapping it up. We had a few laughs, along the way, as someone or another either mucked up his or her lines, or did not get the task they were performing quite right. At break-time the audience of lookers-on was swelled by some five hundred milling and pushing pupils, but by four o'clock this part of the filming was completed.

They then turned their attention to the show sheep. They were filmed having their faces and legs washed, their coats carded and trimmed, and then being walked on the halters. At five, they left. Three and a half hours work altogether – yet we were told that our television debut would run for only about six or seven minutes.

On the Sunday before the show I carded and trimmed the two ewes and our show ram called Duke. The ram had been pushed out of the limelight because he was not expected to do very well at the show – certainly not as well as our two prize ewes. He looked slightly disgruntled, to say the least.

We loaded up the car and trailer, and set off. There were pens and pens of sheep – since over a thousand entries had been received. They represent the best sheep in Britain, and it is very competitive; everyone wants to win. I noticed that the Queen Mother had entered a North Country Cheviot. I kept a look out for her – the Queen Mother, that is – feeding and watering the ewe. Never actually saw her, though. Funny, that. I had a glorious mental picture of her walking very grandly up and down the sheep lines, wearing a smock, swinging a bucket, and with some hay tucked under her arm!

We settled our sheep down, and then left them. I had to teach all the following day, but as soon as school was over I hurried down to the show with my three trusty helpers. I carded and trimmed the sheep once more, and we then went home. Not that I got much sleep. By now, the whole thing was just playing on my mind. The local paper had picked up the story, too, and streams of pupils and parents were taking the day off to come and watch. What if we came last? We would look complete idiots. The night seemed endless, and I tossed and turned. I was up by 4.00 am and at five met the pupils at the school gates. The actual judging was to take place at nine-thirty – but I wanted to be there in plenty of time.

Once more, the ewes were carded and trimmed. Not that they wanted doing, but this familiar task helped settle my nerves. At twenty past nine the Central team arrived and began unpacking all their gear. They did not intend filming the ram, since his chances were slim. We donned our white coats, haltered the sheep, and were ready for off. It was 'ram classes' first. Janet led our shearling ram, Duke, into the ring. I think he had made up his mind that he had something to prove – and I never saw him 'show' better. He walked off with a third place – to everyone's surprise. He came out of the ring with what seemed to me to be a somewhat self-satisfied look on his face.

The tension was mounting. I now wished the crew had actually filmed Duke. A third place was no mean feat. What if the ewes failed altogether? The minutes ticked by, and soon it was time to show them. Adam and I led them into the ring, closely followed by the television crew. The pairs of ewes lined up in the centre, and the judge began his work. Slowly and painstakingly he made his way down the line until it was our turn. They took a lesson out of Duke's book, and really turned it on. They stood superbly and looked a treat. I was sure the judge liked them, but did not dare say anything to Adam, not wanting to raise his hopes.

By now the sun was beating down on us and I was in a real sweat – in more ways than one. It seemed to take an age for the judge to work his way down to the bottom of the line. I watched his every move. He finished looking at the last pair, turned, and walked back towards us. He stopped, took a brief second look at the ewes, then walked further back up the line to look at another pair. My heart sank. Then, unbelievably, he came back down to us . . . and told us to take them to stand at the top of the line.

When we got there, we were standing next to Mr Williamson, with his pair of ewes. We exchanged a few, brief, pleasantries, both too tense to say much. The sweat was dropping off my nose and my nerves were jangling – near to breaking point. I kept glancing towards the judge, hoping against hope that he was not going to change his mind. He signalled to the steward, and it was all over.

We had won.

The steward came over and presented us with the much-prized red certificate and red rosette. The blue certificate and blue rosette went to Mr Williamson. We shook hands, both relieved, in a sense, that it was over. We were then presented with the Champion certificate, Champion rosette, and the trophy for the Champion Kerry Hill Female sheep in the show. As we marched out of the ring the cameras were still on us. Paul Baines came across, beaming all over his face. They set up the final interview, with lighting and sound men in position.

'Well, Mr Terry, you did it! You certainly showed them, didn't you!' said Paul Baines.

'Yes . . . Yes, I suppose we did,' I said, smiling all over my face.

'How did you do it, though? What did the judge see in your sheep?'

'Well, ours were the biggest pair of ewes; very good wool, excellent black and white face and leg markings and upright ears. They looked a real matched pair, too. That's important,' I replied.

'And just what have all these very experienced breeders been saying to you, then? What has the atmosphere been like?'

'Oh, it's been great. We've had quite a bit of encouragement, and quite a few pats on the back,' I replied.

'I understand that you were up at four, and that you and your pupils left school at five, this morning. Has it all been worth it?'

'Oh, yes. It certainly has,' I enthused.

He turned to Adam and the rest of our helpers.

'Now, your pupils do much of the work, I believe, so I must have a word with them, too. Adam, how do you feel about this win?'

'It's great! I felt like doing a lap of honour with the cup!'

'Janet and Stephen, now you didn't actually get to go into the show ring, but you were very much part of the team. How do you feel about it?'

'Fantastic!' said Janet.

'Brilliant!' said Stephen.

That Tuesday afternoon Central Television broadcast the interview. We watched the programme about the show, sitting impatiently through the early part illustrating recent developments in agricultural machinery and so on. Soon it was our turn. The presenter said: 'To win a first at the Royal Show is the achievement of a lifetime. The challenge of getting a "first" is real motivation, something which keeps breeders going, all the year. Our reporter has found some school children who have worked very hard on their school farm, preparing some Kerry Hill sheep for the show. They have already been awarded Champion Females at the Three Counties, but could they win the Royal?'

They then led into the film shot at the farm, going into the actual judging itself. Finally, they ran the interviews with the three pupils and myself. I could not help thinking of all the other episodes they could have filmed – like the pig creating havoc in the home economics room, or the van catching fire on the way to the abattoir! There was enough there to run a series, never mind a news item!

Our champion ewes became real celebrities after that. We had droves of photographers coming to take pictures, and made headlines such as: 'Top of the Form at the Royal Show!'

As we had received the prize for the Champion Kerry Hill Females, it meant that one of our ewes could go a stage further, into the inter-breed championships. There were 1,007 entries in the show, but it is just the champion male and female of each breed which are allowed to enter the inter-breed championship, to find the Champion of

Champions. There were twenty-eight breeds in the show, so it would be some competition. Our very best ewe was Hazel, and she had to be teamed up with the champion Kerry Hill ram, called Big Bill, belonging to Mr Porter. These two would be shown as a team. Big Bill and Hazel would represent the entire Kerry Hill breed. I hoped they would appreciate the honour.

For the second night running I did not sleep at all well. Do not let anyone spin you that yarn about counting sheep. I was thinking of nothing but sheep, and still could not get any sleep. I just kept thinking about the inter-breed competition. All this sheep-showing was playing havoc with my health!

The competition began the following morning, at ten-thirty. A very large crowd – including a number of my pupils – had gathered around the show ring. Mr Porter led out Big Bill, and I led Hazel. They certainly made an attractive pair, both very big sheep, with remarkably similar markings. The twenty-eight teams were now positioned around the show ring. I glanced around, and could see a whole range of different breeds represented there: Oxford Downs, Southdowns, Suffolks, Hampshire Downs, Shropshires, Ryelands, Border Leicesters, Devon and Cornwall Longwool, Clun Forests, Welsh Mountains, Jacobs . . . the list went on and on. We were really going to be up against it.

The judge, resplendent in dark suit and bowler hat, started work. Getting round all twenty-eight pairs was obviously going to take a while, and I was becoming impatient. In time, it was our turn. Our Kerry Hills were doing very well, standing nice and quietly. The judge looked at them carefully, and as he left Mr Porter tipped me a wink and whispered: 'He liked them, didn't he!'

I did not dare answer. The judge immediately returned and gave our sheep a second look, then left and carried on with the other pairs. Mr Porter just smiled, knowingly. The trouble was, I did not know what he knew!

It was another piping hot day, and it took the judge ages

to get round all the breeds. After he had finished he consulted with the steward, with all of us straining our ears to try to hear what was going on. Finally, the steward announced: 'The judge has now drawn up a short-list of six breeds.' It was getting more and more like the Miss World competition. They would be interviewing the sheep, next, asking about their hobbies and ambitions!

The steward announced the short-list. 'These are: Suffolk, Devon and Cornwall Longwool, Kerry Hill . . .' We had made it.

'Come on!' exclaimed Mr Porter, leading Big Bill forwards. I hurried to catch him up. We stood in the centre of the ring with the five other selected breeds, while the judge gave the sheep a further inspection. Then he and the steward went into closed session once more. Finally the decision was made.

'We started yesterday with one thousand and seven entries,' announced the steward. 'From within the various breeds, we found the champions, male and female. Today,

twenty-eight pairs of sheep have been judged to find the Champion of Champions. The judge has had a very hard task. . . .' He droned on and on. 'Come on,' I thought, 'get on with it.' '. . . and so, the results are as follows. The 1982 Inter-breed Champions are . . . the pair of Hampshire Downs.' A round of applause and cheering broke out around the ring. I felt disappointed – but had to admit they were a cracking pair of sheep. The winners were presented with a marvellous trophy, certificates and rosettes.

'The Reserve Inter-breed Champions for 1982 are the pair of . . . Kerry Hills.' Again, applause and cheering broke out from around the ring, and we were ushered forward and presented with certificates and rosettes. I was stunned.

To achieve such honours is, I suppose, the climax of a lifetime's experience. For us, it had been made more difficult, of course, because we had just a few sheep to choose from, not the thousand which many a flock might have. This was only our second year of showing, too. Some farmers could work a lifetime, and still not pull off the elusive prize of a win at the 'Royal'. All the hard work, all the worry, all the graft, now seemed worth it.

We had arrived.

Also published by Farming Press

The sequel to *Pigs in the Playground* is *Calves in the Classroom*.

The cartoons in *Pigs in the Playground* and *Calves in the Classroom* were drawn by Henry Brewis who lives on a cereal and livestock farm in Northumberland.

Farming Press have published three of his books:

Funnywayt' mekalivin' and *The Magic Peasant* are both agricultural stews of cartoons and verses featuring Sep, the universal peasant. His world includes collie dogs, auctioneers, cows, ewes, the long-suffering wife and a range of farm visitors, welcome and unwelcome.

Don't Laugh Till He's Out of Sight is a collection of the best of Henry Brewis's writing, revealing the hazards awaiting anyone venturing on life as a farmer.

Farming Press publish some 50 books on agriculture and animal health. Among these is a small range designed for young people embarking on their agricultural education at school or college. Specifically the level is City and Guilds I and II.

Farm Crops, Graham Boatfield
Farm Livestock, Graham Boatfield
Farm Machinery, Brian Bell
Farm Workshop, Brian Bell
Calculations for Agriculture and Horticulture,
    Graham Boatfield and Ian Hamilton.

If you would like the details of any of these books or a free illustrated catalogue please contact:

Books Department 3, Farming Press Limited,
Wharfedale Road, Ipswich IP1 4LG.